PRAISE FOR T
EFFECT (

GW00683358

"The Butterfly Effect of Money gives a strong reflection on how our choices in life can impact our own financial resilience and mental health. Love the way this has been brought to life through the characters' lived experience. A great read, with lots of little pragmatic guidance on handling financial decisions in the short term, with a strong lens on long-term impact."

Oli O'Donoghue MBE,
Managing Director – Branch Network, HSBC UK

"A most enjoyable book that teaches financial lessons through the lenses of common day challenges and people - it makes sense and is relevant to everybody - no matter what your financial circumstance!"

Jean-Jacques Oelofse,
President, Emerging markets, Wood-Mizer

"Most people are fearful of the daunting subject of personal financial management. These stories unbundle the complexity which if followed will create long term financial and emotional freedom."

Stuart Loxton,
Chief Executive, Superyacht Training Academy

"The Butterfly Effect of Money is a compelling book that follows the lives of four characters and provides ten essential principles for building wealth, including wise decision-making about debt, having a budget, and preparing for the future."

Kobus Kleyn CFP®,
Global Financial Services Thought Leader, South Africa

"A good and entertaining read for all ages. The Butterfly Effect of Money offers insightful life lessons for cultivating good financial discipline. With practical advice and engaging storytelling, it's a must-read for those seeking financial empowerment and long-term stability."

Faeez Davids,
Retail Sales Executive, ABSA

"This is a real masterpiece. It highlights the urgent need for improved financial literacy in all stages of life and sets the reader on the path to greater financial independence."

Kwabena Ofori-Awuah Jnr,
Distribution lead - Customer Partnerships, HSBC UK

"What a lovely book! I really love the way it's such an easy and entertaining read with a very apt message about good financial behaviour."

Fatimah Otto,
DAS Banking Principal, Nedbank Private Wealth

"The Butterfly Effect is a must-read book for young adults and everyone struggling with personal financial management. I literally couldn't put it down until I completed it."

Kantu Achira,
Head, Bancassurance and Wealth Management
propositions, Standard Chartered Bank,
Ghana & Côte d'Ivoire

"I have read many books on money, but this book is different because I could relate to the issues in it. The Butterfly Effect has captured relevant ideas about money and how to solve these pertinent issues. This is a must read to learn some relevant principles about money and how to manage it."

Mark S. Korley,
Workers Compensation Analyst, UPHS

THE BUTTERFLY EFFECT OF MONEY

WHY THE DECISIONS YOU MAKE ABOUT YOUR MONEY MATTER

STEVEN JACOBS

AUTHOR OF "THE NEW MANAGER: HOW TO BECOME A LEADER IN 52 SIMPLE STEPS"

THE BUTTERFLY EFFECT OF MONEY © STEVEN JACOBS

First Edition 2023
Published by: **www.leaderofleaders.com**

The story, all names, characters, and incidents portrayed in this book are fictitious. No identification with actual persons (living or deceased), places, buildings, and products are intended or should be inferred.

Editor: Brenda Burgess
Photograph of the dollar: **www.lisajunerosephotography.co.uk**

ISBN: 978-1-3999-3794-8 (Paperback)

This book is dedicated to my four beautiful children, whom I love with all my heart.

Contents

Forward

I am writing to express my sincere gratitude for the book, "The Butterfly Effect of Money." Being a banker myself, I have had the experience of seeing first-hand what good and bad money management can lead to. However, I believe that if I personally had the opportunity to learn what is so well captured in this book early in my life, it would have been incredibly valuable to me, both personally and professionally.

I particularly appreciate the way stories are used to illustrate the key concepts of money management. They are engaging and relatable, and they help to bring the concepts to life in a way that dry financial advice simply cannot. I also appreciate the way the importance of how small decisions that you start with, can have a big impact over time towards the life you desire, is emphasized. This is a message that I believe is essential for everyone to hear, regardless of their financial situation.

I am surely going to share the learnings from the book with my family and with individuals who I can impact. For me, 'The butterfly effect of money' is –

'A quality practical guide to the ripple effect of individual money management and the choices one can make towards their desired life!'

I believe it will be a valuable resource for anyone who wants to improve their financial situation. Thank you again for writing such an informative and inspiring book.

Sanjay Rughani, CEO
Standard Chartered Bank - Uganda

Introduction

When I was a child, my grandfather was a caretaker at a secondary school in South Africa. He and my gran lived on the school premises, and my brothers and I thoroughly enjoyed the weekends we spent with them. We had a fantastic time exploring the school property as there were so many unusual places to investigate: tennis courts, an Olympic-sized swimming pool, eight sports fields, and loads of classrooms, although the latter were mostly locked! There was so much to do.

On one occasion my brothers and I found a strange machine which looked like something out of a science fiction novel. We had no idea what it did, but it had a big handle so naturally we grabbed this and started to turn it. Suddenly a tennis ball shot out of a hole in the machine! Fortunately, none of us had been peering into the hole at that point, otherwise there would have been many tears and a swollen eye. We instinctively knew that we were not allowed to play with this contraption but did so anyway and that made it even more exciting. I didn't understand the point of the tennis machine then but reflecting on it now, I realise it must have helped thousands of children to improve their tennis skills.

Similarly, the purpose of this book is to help you understand that you have many opportunities to make great choices, even in the middle of really challenging situations. I believe that too many people write off their future selves based on their regrets. Many make a mistake, or miss an opportunity, and for the rest of their lives they punish themselves for the wrong decisions they've made, but it does not need to be this way. We should take courage from history. It shows us that humans are resilient, and that despite disasters they find ways to overcome all challenges and rebuild their lives. In my view, we are made to be overcomers! The world is full of wonderful examples of this.

In the course of my work, I have met countless people with money challenges. Some of them have been very wealthy and others not at all. One of my customers was a senior executive in a large insurance corporation; he had everything he needed, and yet went bankrupt in a space of four months due to a gambling addiction. I have seen others with comparatively few financial challenges who resigned themselves to poverty because they believed that they would never get free from debt as it was their lot in life, and that is what it became. In comparison I can also think of many people who were washed up and had nothing left. Their finances were a mess, and their houses had been repossessed and yet they were able to rebuild their lives and became even wealthier than before.

My hope is that throughout this book you will see that your present choices can positively affect your long-term finances. Wisdom looks at the past, present and the future when it comes to decision making. If, like me, you have made an incorrect choice in the past and have spent many a sleepless night troubled by it. I want you to know that there is always an opportunity in your 'today' to make a better choice, and this choice will start you on the journey of turning things around.

Many years back I knew a man who was obsessed with getting rich. He worked three jobs and never had one minute to spare. He was making an absolute fortune, but at what cost? He never spent time with family or friends and even his girlfriend hardly saw him. One day he asked her to marry him, and she said yes. I am sure she thought that things would change now that they were engaged, but he carried on putting money before everything else. This resulted in his fiancé breaking off the engagement.

During that time of devastation, he had a breakdown. However, because of that pain, he made some fundamental changes to his lifestyle. Today he is happily married and has two beautiful children. He no longer works three jobs and yet he is a financial success. His lifestyle choices have enabled him to spend time with his family and friends, and this has supplied far more joy and contentment than the stress he carried when he was consumed with money.

Life is truly more important than money and, as my friend learnt, when you devote your life and time in the pursuit of wealth, you lose both yourself and the people you care about in the process. Cherish the times you have with your family and friends, and do not pressurise yourself to get rich. Instead relax, apply the right financial principles, and enjoy your life—the money will come.

Why the butterfly effect of money?

In 1972 meteorologist Edward Lorenz published a paper titled, *'Predictability: Does the Flap of a Butterfly's Wings in Brazil Set Off a Tornado in Texas?'*

It is fascinating to consider how such a slight change in the weather system can result in massive storms further away, yet that is exactly what his research was pointing to. The concept has resulted in books and movies which illustrate that if a person makes a minor change now, it will impact everything further down the line. In many cases the future turns out more chaotic than they'd anticipated. If we pinpoint a turbulent situation in the present and look back in time to find the origin, we will inevitably find a very insignificant starting point, a small flutter.

In 2008 my wife and I were quarrelling daily; we had two young children at the time and our marriage was close to breaking down. The conflict was a result of having very little money to live on as we had too much debt. In reflecting on where it all went wrong, we saw that this was a result of choices we'd made years earlier. Much like the butterfly effect we were experiencing the consequence of many decisions made in the past. The lesson I learnt in that difficult period was that it is easier to get into debt than out of it. Fortunately, we got through that time and now we are happily married with four beautiful children.

Over the years I have been approached by people from all walks of life who have had similar financial struggles. Yet this kind of experience is so unnecessary. Life does not need to be this way! I believe that we can avoid all this trauma by knowing how to make wise financial decisions. But how do we learn how to make these decisions, and where do we get the relevant preparation, training, and qualifications?

In reflecting on my childhood, I asked myself, "Who had taught me about money? Did school prepare me for all the twists and turns that lay ahead? Did my parents share their personal experience?"

The truth is that I was not prepared for what lay ahead when I first started earning money, as has been the case for many others just like me. I have written this book in the hope that it will bridge the knowledge gap and enable many to make great financial decisions from the start, building their wealth and avoiding the pitfalls of being in debt.

In this book you will read about the lives of four fictional characters from diverse financial backgrounds. You will get to see first-hand the decisions they make about their money and the consequences that follow. The book also captures the daily emotional trauma faced by people all over the world because of their financial difficulties. It is my hope that understanding both the happiness and the trauma these four characters go through, will be the catalyst that causes you to make wise decisions about your money.

It is within your power to take a stand and do something spectacular with whatever is in your hands, no matter how much or how little it is. Most of all, may this book help you to grow in wisdom and, as a result, help you build your wealth.

1. The Story

Winter is not a fun time to be at school. Every part of every person just wants to be at home in a nice warm cosy bed. Fortunately, on the day our story begins, the school radiators were working well. As a rule, students clustered around these radiators whenever possible, only drifting back to their desks with great reluctance when summoned by their teachers. This day was different: these students would gladly have stood outside in the chilly wind instead of being stuck in the middle of a dispute between their teacher and the class bully.

Mrs Olivia Ward stood at the back of the classroom, next to Jason's desk. Her cheeks were flushed, and her eyes blazed for she had entered the point of no return. "Just who do you think you are, young man?"

Moments earlier Jason had sworn at her after she berated him for not doing his homework.

"How dare you speak to me like that!" she said.

Jason stood up and cursed her again, his face so close to hers that she instinctively took a step backwards and almost lost her footing over someone's backpack. Every other person in the room wanted to do something to protect Mrs Ward yet their fear of Jason immobilised them.

Suddenly, Emmanuel, who wore unfashionable hand-me-downs and was by far the smallest kid in the class, jumped to his feet. He positioned himself between Mrs Ward and Jason, as if to protect her, and then stood his ground.

"Get out the way you fool," Jason screamed, pushing against Emmanuel's chest.

"No, leave Mrs Ward alone," Emmanuel replied, trying to sound firm but not able to hide the quiver in his voice.

Jason grabbed him violently by the collar and Emmanuel braced himself for a beating, yet just as Jason was about to take his anger out on him, Jennifer stood up on the other side of the room.

"Leave him alone!" she yelled.

Jennifer was the most popular girl in the class, and it did not take long for the rest to join in and shout at Jason. To everyone's relief he released Emmanuel, grabbed his bag, and stormed out of the classroom. As soon as he reached the corridor, Jason began thinking about his mum and how she ridiculed him every day. Mrs Ward had the same effect on him. These thoughts made him even angrier, and he hurried to get off the school property. His rage built up until, unable to hold it in anymore, he punched the nearest wall and found satisfaction in the pain. In doing so he reopened a wound that had just healed, and blood oozed down his fingers. This was nothing new. His home life was tough, and he had received many beatings from his dad before he died; his mum meanwhile had verbally abused him his whole life and the ongoing trauma had crushed his spirit. Jason had learnt to go it alone.

Olivia Ward left the room in tears and headed to the principal's office. Jason was a problem that had to be dealt with and whatever compassion she had felt for him was now submerged by feelings of anger. She'd never been spoken to or threatened like that in her life! Growing up, she'd had a loving dad and mum who cared deeply for her and spoke politely to her and to each other. There was always food on the table and at night she slept undisturbed in her own bed. Her parents were her greatest cheerleaders and they supported her in every step she took. When she graduated as a teacher, they were the first to encourage her that she would excel in her career and help so many students. Olivia had never known domestic conflict and she had never experienced abuse. Now, confronted with the ripple effect of its destruction, all she wanted was justice. How dare this young man swear at her!

Meanwhile, in the classroom, Jennifer walked swiftly across to check on Emmanuel.

"Are you ok?" she asked quietly.

He nodded and looked at the floor as he straightened his shirt, then returned to his seat and sat down. The rest of the class crowded around Jennifer to commend her for her bravery.

"Why did you do that?" Zara asked, with a look of disgust on her face.

"I couldn't let the poor guy get beaten up," Jennifer said quickly, and Zara giggled.

"What's so funny?" Jennifer asked.

"He certainly is poor," Zara snickered.

Jennifer glared at her as she hadn't intended her words to be taken quite so literally and she failed to see any humour in the situation. She wiped her sweaty palms down her designer jeans; she always wore expensive clothes as her family were exceptionally wealthy. She'd heard the gossip that her father was a billionaire who owned several successful businesses, and she never bothered to deny it.

The members of the school tribunal were unanimous in their decision: Jason was to be expelled with immediate effect. He had a book's worth of offences and Mrs Ward was not the first teacher at whom he had sworn. There was a rumour that he had even slapped a teacher at his previous school.

2. Jason's Journey

Jason was angry at being expelled from school, but at the same time he did not really care. "What a complete waste of time," he muttered to himself. "I don't need the school. They teach things that have no relevance in the real world. What does Geography, History, and Maths have to do with anything? The only people that ever use what they learn in school are teachers because they can't get real jobs." The more he spoke the angrier he got. "Who does Mrs Ward think she is? I don't need to go to school to be a success, I will prove her wrong."

The system had sucked him in and spat him out, and he had no idea where to start or what to do. **He only knew that because he was no longer at school, he needed to get a job. But although he applied for many positions, Jason didn't get any interviews as his qualifications and experience did not meet the selection criteria.** He wished it were possible to chat to his father who had passed away years back. At the time Jason had thought 'good riddance,' yet now he felt differently. Tears welled up and ran down his cheeks and he felt disgusted with himself for succumbing to a moment of weakness. His mum was still around, but he had no relationship with her. All the years of mental abuse had built an impenetrable concrete wall that blocked out anything she said.

Jason was desperate to get a job, so when he saw an advert which said, *Bricklayer wanted; no experience necessary*, he immediately rang the number.

The telephone call went better than he'd expected and led to an interview. The recruiter liked something about Jason and offered him the job. He would start on the first of February.

3. The Temptation

Jason woke up exceedingly early on Monday morning to get ready for his first day at work. He was anxious as he did not know what to expect. The sun was just rising as he arrived on site. He was met by Mike, the supervisor who had hired him. Mike asked a couple of questions to see how much training Jason would need to get up to scratch, then instructed him to shadow Brett, a beast of a man who did not suffer fools gladly. Jason had always been the toughest guy at school but here amongst the men he felt like a small boy. His first rude awakening took place within five minutes when Brett bellowed at him (with quite a few expletives) for picking up a brick too slowly.

At the end of his first day the supervisor gave Jason some feedback: "Make sure that you are on time in the morning and don't let me catch you loafing or taking shortcuts, or you are out of here. Understood?"

Jason nodded.

"Good, I will see you tomorrow."

Jason was exhausted but somehow reached home and lay down on his bed. He was not sure that he would be able to make another day, let alone a whole week. The next day, he struggled to get out of bed. Every muscle ached, yet he pushed through the pain and went to work. It was another tough day, and he was sworn at even more. At one stage when he dropped a brick, he thought he was going to get punched. He made it through the day, but his body felt battered. The days rolled into weeks and only the thought of getting his first salary of one thousand two hundred and fifty pounds kept him going. It would be the most money he had ever made in his life.

He expected to get cash but a couple of days before pay day, the supervisor asked for his bank details.

"I don't have a bank account," Jason replied.

The supervisor was nonplussed. "You don't have an account?"

"No," Jason said, puzzled.

"What are you waiting for, Jason? Go get one!" the supervisor said, shaking his head in disbelief.

On the way home, Jason walked into the first bank he came across. He was met by an advisor named Ayesha who smiled and asked how she could help him.

"I want to open an account," Jason said.

Ayesha responded, "You can use either your computer or mobile phone to open the account."

Jason responded, "I don't have a computer and I don't know how to use my phone."

"Let me show you how to use it," she said as she put her hand out for his phone.

Jason handed it over much to his bemusement.

Looking at the phone Ayesha realised that it was an outdated version with no access to the internet. She was still not deterred. She handed it back and led him to one of the bank's own computers and invited him to sit down. However, it soon became clear that he would need her guidance throughout the process. Jason had so many questions and he lacked computer skills, so the ten-minute journey took over an hour. Jason was annoyed when Ayesha asked for proof of his address. "Why would I carry that with me?" he asked.

Ayesha explained that without it the account could not be opened that day. Proof of address was a regulatory requirement.

Jason went home. He was frustrated by the delay and the knowledge that he had no documents showing his address. He needed a letter from his mum as she was the owner of the house and paid the bills. He didn't want to ask her for anything, and it irritated him that he needed her help, yet he had no choice in the matter as he couldn't get hold of his salary until he had a bank account. When he spoke to his mum that evening, she replied that she wanted him to pay rent, and eventually he reluctantly agreed on three hundred and fifty pounds a month. At this, she gladly handed over the letter confirming that he lived in the house. She also gave him a recent utility bill with their address on it.

The next day Jason was back at the bank to open the account. Ayesha explained to him that it was a basic account with no lending facilities, but he didn't care; all he wanted was his money. The formalities completed; he gave his new account number to his company. On pay day Jason was so excited to see how much money there was in his account, but he was also surprised how quickly he spent it. Within three weeks he was broke and the wait for the next pay day was unbearable and awkward. **Jason thought that he should set a limit on how much he spent each week to ensure that he did not overspend.** It took a few more months before he got it right, but by month nine he had mastered this, and he was starting to save a little each month.

One day Jason was on his way to get lunch at his local takeaway when a large poster caught his eye: *Need Money Fast? Look No Further.* In smaller print below the bold headline, he read: *Why not speak to a salesperson inside the store to see if you qualify?* He started to think that this could be a sign for him. A few days earlier he'd met up with Angus, a friend who was selling a two-seater BMW with 135,312 miles on the clock. The mileage was high, but Angus had taken exceptionally diligent care of the car. As far as Jason could see, it was in excellent condition. He had taken the car for a test drive and instantly wanted to have it. It was everything he had dreamed of, and he was particularly impressed by the acceleration and the leather seats. Angus wanted two thousand pounds, but Jason was eight hundred pounds short. Angus had assured him that he would not sell it to anyone else and would wait until Jason could afford it. Now, staring at the sign, he felt excitement building up. They might give him the eight hundred pounds he needed! At the same time, he felt nervous, as if he were about to do something wrong.

4. The Shortcut

Need money fast? Look No Further. The advert seemed simple enough but there had to be a catch. Jason walked into the furniture store to find out more. The young saleswoman gave him a gleaming smile.

"Hello, I'm Lucy. What's your name?"

"Jason. I would like to know more about the money you are advertising."

Lucy sprang into action. She was well trained and knew how to position the offering in such a way that it appealed to the customer with whom she was speaking.

"Sure Jason. From start to finish, the entire process should take no longer than ten minutes. How does that sound?"

Jason responded, "Sounds good to me." He really wanted the loan. Trying hard not to appear desperate, he nonchalantly ran his fingers through his hair.

Lucy picked up on his nervousness. To put him at his ease, she told him a little about herself then spoke confidently about her product and how she was qualified to sell it.

And she then asked him a crucial question. "What would you like to spend the money on?"

He blurted out: "A car."

"What car are you thinking about buying?"

"A friend's BMW Z3," he said excitedly.

Lucy said, "I know that car, a friend of mine has one and it's magnificent."

Jason interjected, "And fast!"

Lucy smiled in acknowledgement. She had been trained to get potential customers to focus on the purpose of the loan as there was then a much higher chance of them taking it. Her strategy was working perfectly: Jason became engrossed in the conversation and found himself describing everything he loved about the vehicle, and this just made him want it more. Lucy helpfully clarified all the details on the loan and guided him through the online application. Despite her explanation, Jason did not realise the long-term impact of the decision he was about to make in that furniture store. There certainly is no such thing as easy money, but he still needed to learn that lesson. This would be his very first taste of debt.

Lucy told Jason that the system had approved him for an amount of up to one thousand, two hundred pounds as he met all the criteria.

"How much would you like to borrow?" she asked smoothly.

Jason replied, "one thousand, two hundred pounds please." His head was spinning. He only needed eight hundred pounds but was excited about getting the extra four hundred. Lucy went on to explain the terms and conditions in detail (she called them the T's and C's) and kept checking in with Jason that he understood what she was saying. He nodded his head in agreement each time but was not actually listening to her, as all he could think about was the car.

Jason tried to rush Lucy by asking, "Where can I sign to get the loan?"

Lucy responded politely, "Jason, before you sign, I have to go through all the T's and C's to ensure that you understand the legal agreement that you are about to sign."

Jason nodded.

Without hurrying, Lucy continued, "The loan needs to be repaid over twelve months, in monthly instalments of one hundred and twenty-three pounds and thirty pence, the annual percentage rate is forty nine percent, and the total amount that would be repaid is one thousand, four hundred and seventy-nine pounds and fifty-seven pence. Do you have any questions so far?"

Jason responded, "No, everything sounds great." Yet all Jason had heard was that the instalments were one hundred and twenty-three pounds and thirty pence a month. This sounded manageable.

Lucy went on to explain all the clauses and what the penalties would be if he failed to make a payment. Then she asked Jason if he would like to go ahead with the loan. **Jason nodded, even though he did not really understand the full implications of what he was signing. He really wanted the money.** He signed all the documents, and the loan was paid into his bank account while he was still in the store. Jason walked out feeling extremely happy as he now had the money to buy his car. He called Angus and told him the great news and arranged to meet him. The meeting with Angus was bittersweet as there were a few hidden costs that Jason had not known about. Angus explained that the car had recently passed the MOT test.

This mandatory UK test proved that the vehicle was roadworthy, and the MOT needed renewing every year. He explained that if Jason were caught driving the car with an expired MOT, he would face a steep fine. Angus also said he would have to pay road tax and insurance.

Jason had no idea that he had to pay this but was relieved that he had taken the extra four hundred pounds as the road tax was three hundred and sixty pounds, and the insurance would be fifty-nine pounds a month. He made all the payments, and the vehicle was registered in his name. This had been an expensive process, but the euphoria of having his own car made it that much easier.

Every month, the loan instalment was drawn out of his bank account and by the time he'd made the tenth payment, he was struggling to make ends meet. He borrowed fifty pounds from a friend at work when he ran short of cash, but figured he could pay it back at the end of the month as he had finished repaying the one thousand two-hundred-pound loan.

But, at month end, although his salary went into his bank account, he saw that, yet another one hundred and twenty-three pounds and thirty pence had been taken out. Surely this was not right. Panic set in and Jason went to his bank to find out where his money had gone. There was an exceptionally long queue and when he finally reached the counter, Jason asked why they had taken one hundred and twenty-three pounds and thirty pence out of his account. The bank teller asked to see Jason's identification and verified that it was him. She then checked his account and went on to explain that the one hundred and twenty-three pounds and thirty pence was an instalment for a loan he had taken. Jason snapped back that it was already repaid and asked why the bank had stolen his money. The teller had no answers for him and told him to speak to the company that had issued the loan. A small argument ensued but it was one Jason was never going to win.

Jason fumed as he made his way back to the furniture store to speak to Lucy. She was there but was less friendly than she had been a few months earlier. She told him that he would need to go to the service department as she only dealt with new loans. By now Jason was cursing loudly. He had totally lost his patience, and a security guard approached him to tell him to keep his voice down. The more the security guard spoke, the louder and madder Jason got. A scuffle ensued and Jason was escorted off the premises with a warning that either he calmed down or he would not be welcomed back into the store.

That night Jason tried to work out why he had been charged one hundred and twenty-three pounds and thirty pence as over the previous ten months he had already paid one thousand, two hundred and thirty-three pounds. In fact, they owed *him* money as he had only loaned one thousand, two hundred pounds. He needed to get his money back urgently as he did not have enough to make it through the month, let alone pay his friend fifty pounds.

The following day he returned to the store. The security guard recognised Jason and watched his every move as he waited in the service queue. Eventually it was his turn, and he was assisted by a service consultant named Zee. When she asked for his identification, Jason handed it over and tried to explain his frustration.

Zee interrupted him. "I first need to bring up your account on my system," she said.

Jason waited while she punched the keys and looked through all the notes; he gave the impression of being patient but inside he was screaming.

After a while, he asked: "Will this take long?"

"Just a minute sir, I will be with you shortly," Zee said courteously, still staring at her screen.

Jason looked at his watch and saw that many minutes had already passed. He was sure this delay was retribution for his antics the previous day.

Zee eventually said. "I can see that you have taken a one thousand, two-hundred-pound loan with us. How can I help you today?"

"I want to know why your company stole one hundred and twenty-three pounds and thirty pence of my money," he stated flatly.

"I'm sorry but you are incorrect," Zee said, looking uncomfortable. "We simply took the instalment that you owed us and..."

Jason interrupted before she could finish her sentence. "I have already paid one thousand, two hundred and thirty-three pounds!"

She checked the documents on her system while Jason tapped the counter agitatedly.

"Yes, you have. Here in your contract on page two, clause fourteen, it states that the annual percentage rate is forty nine percent and that your instalments are one hundred and twenty-three pounds and thirty pence over twelve months and the total amount repayable is one thousand, four hundred and seventy-nine pounds, fifty-seven pence. I can see that you initialled next to the clause and have also signed the document, so you were told about this."

Jason shouted, "That is not what happened, I was never told about these charges!"

"Sir, please don't speak to me like that. I am trying to help you understand what happened. The contract you have signed shows that you were aware of the charges."

Jason took a deep breath. "I may have signed the forms, but I did not know about these charges."

Zee responded, "Jason, I feel like we are going in circles here. Is there anything further that I can help you with?"

He swore under his breath and left the store.

Jason vowed never to use that company's services again in his life. However, when his mum asked him for the month's rent the following day, he realised that he was in a financial mess. How was he going to make it through the month with so little money? The straw that broke the camel's back was when Jason received a reminder letter that his road tax was due in two months' time. The pressure he was facing was unbearable and he punched the wall in frustration. He decided that the only way out of this mess was another loan.

5. The Chokehold

The next day Jason walked back into the store. He resented the fact that he had to get another loan but at the same time he was relieved that at least he would have some money to pay for his expenses. As Lucy was not available, another salesperson guided him through the process, and he was approved for a further one-thousand-pound loan, however one hundred and twenty-three pounds and thirty pence of it would be used to settle the previous loan.

The salesperson went through all the terms and conditions very carefully to make sure that Jason understood what they meant. The annual percentage rate was now sixty-nine-point-nine percent. The total charges for the loan were four hundred and seventeen pounds, sixty-two pence, and the total amount he would repay would be one thousand, four hundred and seventeen pounds, sixty-two pence; the instalment would be one hundred and eighteen pounds and fourteen pence over 12 months.

Jason agreed to all the terms and conditions and signed the forms, after which eight hundred and seventy-six pounds, and seventy pence was paid into his account. He left the store feeling extremely angry that he had to do this, but he felt that he had no choice but to take the loan. The following day he paid his friend back the fifty pounds he owed him. Jason then rang the call centre number on his reminder letter and found out that the road tax would be three hundred and sixty pounds. The call agent also advised that his MOT was also due in two months' time. Jason cursed again as this was yet another charge he'd forgotten about. He arranged to have the MOT done and was told that his vehicle had failed the test. It needed its oil filter replaced and had to have new brake pads installed. Jason enquired what this was all going to cost him, and the amount was three hundred and twenty-two pounds and sixty pence. He reluctantly told them to go ahead as he needed his car to get to work. His month was completely ruined when he received a letter from his insurance company advising about his annual renewal, the monthly premium would be increasing from fifty-nine to sixty-seven pounds a month. He figured that this was due to an earlier claim he had made to have his windscreen replaced.

Seven months later Jason's bank account was overdrawn by twenty-four pounds, and he received an SMS telling him that his account was in an unarranged overdraft. He needed to rectify it, or the insurance payment would be rejected. Jason panicked. **The SMS sounded serious. At that moment, he decided to get another loan from the furniture store.**

He met with a consultant called Eric who followed the familiar steps of the loan application. This time the loan was declined. Jason could not believe what he was hearing, and immediately asked to see Lucy. Eric insisted that it would make no difference, but Jason was having none of it. Fortunately, Lucy was in the store at the time and agreed to speak to him.

"How may I help you?" Lucy asked.

"I just want a loan. I've been speaking to Eric, who is incompetent. Please can you sort it out."

She looked at the screen, muttered something to herself, and finally took a deep breath as if she knew what was coming, "I am sorry sir, but you do not qualify for a loan with us as you don't meet the criteria anymore."

Jason was struggling to keep his temper in check, and he could see that a security guard was slowly walking towards him. Eric must have tipped him off.

"I have taken two loans with you, why is it a problem now?" Jason spluttered.

Lucy replied, "Sorry sir, your credit score does not allow us to loan you this money."

It was like the kiss of death to Jason. There was nothing he could do.

"Is it possible to borrow a bit less?" he said a little desperately.

Lucy responded, "I am afraid not at this time, but you may be able to apply for a loan at a later date."

"What must I do?"

Lucy started to explain how he could improve his credit score.

Jason interrupted rudely: "I am not interested in how to improve my credit score; I want to know what I must do now to get money to live on? Your company has thrown me under the bus!"

Lucy said that she understood why he was upset, but reiterated they would not be able to help him as he no longer met the criteria. At this point, he kicked the counter and started swearing at Lucy. The security guard quickly intervened and escorted Jason off the premises.

Jason had to find a way to get more money and remembered that he read somewhere that he could get a credit card. He went to his bank to find out more. A consultant took him through a forty-five-minute application process, but, after all that, the bank declined his application.

He was furious and vowed to close all his accounts. The consultant empathised with him and explained that he did not meet the bank's criteria for a credit card. Jason started swearing at the consultant and would not stop despite the many requests for him to calm down, which resulted in a security guard escorting him out the building. Later that afternoon he did an online search to see if there was another way to get a loan. He went through an online application and was relieved when he saw that he would be approved by a company he had never heard of before. **They offered him a short-term loan of two hundred pounds with an annual percentage rate of a thousand percent. The credit charge for the loan would cost ninety-eight pounds and eleven pence, which was a huge amount. Jason did not care as he was desperate**

for the money. He accepted the loan and signed the agreement.

He would repay the loan in three instalments of ninety-nine pounds and thirty-seven pence and by the time the loan was repaid, the two hundred pounds would have cost him two hundred and ninety-eight pounds and eleven pence.

The following day Jason checked his account and saw that although the two hundred pounds had been paid into his account, the insurance payment of sixty-seven pounds had been rejected. He was furious! His account had money in it, so why had they rejected the insurance payment? He immediately rang the bank's call centre and had to listen to an annoying tune for fifteen minutes before he could speak to someone. The consultant, whose name was John, greeted him politely and asked a few questions to verify that it was in fact Jason on the phone before asking the reason for the call. It only took a few minutes for Jason to pour out all his frustration. He said the bank had better pay the insurance company as he had done nothing wrong and if they did not, they would be liable if anything happened to his car as he was now uninsured. John was trained to deal with frustrated customers and was able to maintain his composure throughout the conversation. He explained that the insurance payment had been rejected because Jason's account was overdrawn and his deposit of two hundred pounds had not gone into his account quickly enough. Jason tried many different angles to get the bank to agree to make the insurance payment, but they would not budge. He even threatened to close his account, whereupon John politely reiterated that he understood Jason's frustration, and advised him to contact the insurance company to arrange payment, as they would have a process for situations like this. Jason hung up in frustration and punched the wall beside him.

The next morning, he called the insurance company to explain what had happened and told them that the bank had mistakenly rejected the payment. The insurance consultant assured him that they could take payment over the phone and that would sort everything out. Jason's nerves began to calm down as the consultant took his card details and received the payment of sixty-seven pounds.

Over the months that followed, Jason continued to accumulate short term loans and soon his total outstanding debt was four thousand, two hundred and thirty-four pounds. He tried to get other loans but was declined everywhere. With all his options exhausted, he had no choice but to swallow his pride and ask friends for money.

Five of his close friends were each prepared to loan him one hundred pounds, but none of them knew that he'd approached the others. He then found other friends who would each loan him fifty pounds. Overall, he managed to get eight hundred and fifty pounds that he had no intention of ever paying back. He refused to pay his mum her rent of three hundred and fifty pounds, and he didn't bother depositing any of the cash he got into his account. The result was that all the debit orders for his loans were returned by the bank 'due to insufficient funds.'

Letters of demand arrived, but he ignored them. He received phone calls suggesting he see a financial consultant, but he refused as he didn't see the need.

The stress was unbearable. He had become a victim of the debt spiral where his answer to debt was to try and borrow more money to pay the previous debt off, and this only resulted in more debt. Finally, a county court judgement arrived telling him of the minimum amount he was to pay; not doing so would incur further legal action. Jason panicked and felt that he had no choice but to sell his car. He only got nine hundred pounds for it and used the money to pay off some of his debt. He then arranged with the lenders to pay off the remainder of the money he owed in small instalments.

Unfortunately, the relief was only temporary as the debts soon piled up again. In his frustration he often reflected on where it all went wrong, and he concluded that the furniture store was to blame. How he wished he had never crossed paths with them; life would have been so different. Yet despite this revelation he could not get free from the chokehold debt had on him, and his financial struggles continued for the remainder of his days.

6. Jennifer's Journey

Jennifer's day at school had been extremely chaotic and she desperately wanted to speak to her dad about it as she felt that he would understand and give her solid advice. The wait was agonising but at last she heard the front door open. She raced into the hallway, only to see her mother hanging up her coat. Sue was back unexpectedly early from her medical practice.

"Hi mum," Jennifer said brightly. "Where's dad?"

"He's working late tonight. Why?"

"Oh, I just wanted his advice about something that happened at school."

"Tell me."

Jennifer knew there was a good chance that her mum would overreact when she heard the story but, in the end, she told her everything.

"Jen, do we need to worry about this boy? Is he going to do anything to you? Why don't you stay at home for the next few days until this ruckus blows over? What is the school doing about it? I've a good mind to call them tomorrow!"

Jennifer's fears had been well founded. Her mum was a habitual worrier, and the barrage of questions drowned her spirit. Earlier she'd thought she had done something great and that her parents would be proud of her, yet now she felt frustrated and misunderstood.

"Mum—please don't phone the school. You are only going to make it worse. I am ok, honestly."

She knew her mum would text her dad straight away and tell him about Jason. She wanted to chat to her dad too. Reuben was an incredibly busy man, and most nights he got home at around 9 p.m., grabbed a plate of food and disappeared into his study with his laptop. She'd had grown accustomed to this and knew that her only window of opportunity was during the first ten minutes after he walked in through the front door. If she tried to talk to him after this, he always said he was busy; his laptop would be open, and it was clear his work had priority. If she protested, he merely reminded her that the great life they were living with all its luxuries came at a cost and that cost was his time. **Jennifer appreciated the beautiful house, and it was nice to have whatever her heart desired, yet inside she felt empty. No number of possessions could fill that hole—she just wanted more time with her dad.**

That night things were different. Reuben, having been primed by his wife, cancelled his late night at the office and arrived home at 7 pm.

He sat down with Jennifer in the lounge and asked, "What happened at the school?"

Jennifer told her dad the whole story then said, "Do you think I did the right thing?" Secretly she was hoping he would understand and acknowledge her bravery, but he became even more distraught than her mum had.

"Jennifer, is this not the same Emmanuel who was featured in the newspaper after your school's entrepreneurship day? He lives in a rundown part of town! You should know better than to get involved with the poor. How many times do I have to tell you this? It only leads to trouble."

She was surprised at her father's comments and said, "Dad, why are you speaking about Emmanuel, when it was Jason who was…"

Reuben grew increasingly agitated and cut his daughter off mid-sentence, "No Jennifer, it is wrong, you should not have got involved. What if something had happened to you? You have such a bright future ahead of you."

Jennifer burst into tears and rushed off to her room. She felt that her parents had blown the whole thing out of proportion, and instinctively knew that they would call the school in the morning.

The next day Jennifer's fears came true: her dad rang the school principal who assured him that the school was aware of the situation and that they were dealing with it. When the call ended Reuben felt much better, but still warned Jennifer to stay clear of Emmanuel and keep out of other people's business. From now on, she had to focus on her own life.

A few weeks later, a rumour went around the school that Jason had been expelled. Jennifer shared the news with her parents and was puzzled when they showed no surprise. They merely agreed that the rumour was true.

The truth was that Jennifer's parents really did want the best for her. Their daughter's life had been mapped out since her birth; both her parents were Oxford alumni, and they were determined that she would also add this prestigious name to her resumé. Her dad had not been born to wealth and had worked incredibly hard to get to where he was and, equally impressively, her mum had built up her medical practice from scratch. Their daughter's path should be easier than theirs, they felt, and, even though they could easily afford private education, they had chosen to send Jennifer to a public school as they wanted to ensure that she remained grounded. However, her parents also organised private tutors every day after school and this specialised help propelled Jennifer to the top of her class.

Jennifer applied to become a student at Oxford University and, although the requirements were tough, her excellent A-level results meant she was accepted. She was to follow in her mum's footsteps and become a GP. Her time at university was uneventful and with all the tutors her parents provided, she managed to pass every year. Yet something inside of her felt empty; it was as if she lacked purpose. During her final year, the emptiness grew, and she kept asking herself, "When did I last feel alive?" The only answer she could give was the day she'd stood up for Emmanuel. This was the start of her epiphany. She knew her emptiness would be satisfied if she could help those in need.

Jennifer graduated and in the five years that followed she completed the foundation program and her general practice specialist training. She was finally fully qualified to practice medicine. Her mum and dad were bursting with pride. Their daughter had done it! To celebrate, Reuben booked a table at an upmarket restaurant on a country estate as he knew it was Jennifer's favourite.

Before they went out that night, her mum opened a bottle of champagne to toast her achievement.

"Well done my baby, I cannot wait for you to join my practice, everything is ready for you."

"Mum, I must speak to you," said Jennifer.

"What is it my love?"

"Mum, now that I have qualified, I want to make a difference in the world, and…"

Sue was quick to interrupt. "Absolutely, you are certainly going to make a difference!"

Jennifer tried again. "Mum, I want to join a non-profit organisation and help the poor."

"What?" said her mum as if she had misheard her.

"I want to join a non-profit organisation. The research I have done shows there are some real needs out there."

"Don't be ridiculous Jennifer. Why do you want to waste your time doing that? Everything is already set up for you to join my practice."

Ruben took this as his cue to get involved. "Let's chat about it on the way to the restaurant."

"Dad, I really want to make a difference. This is something that means so much to me."

They got into his car and all the way to the restaurant the conversation went back and forth. Jennifer's parents did their utmost to talk some sense into her.

"Well," Sue eventually said, "I do see how passionate you are about helping the needy. What you're suggesting isn't such a bad idea."

This did not go down well with Reuben. "I did not put our daughter through the best university so that she could waste her education on the poor!"

It was a stalemate with no winners, but all the same he continued to badger Jennifer.

"Why do you want to waste your talent on the poor? We have all worked so hard to get here," he said irritably.

"Why are you so judgmental?" Jennifer replied. "Weren't you poor when you grew up?"

The question cut him to the heart. He had been poor during his schooling years and had been teased and picked on as he often had holes in his shoes and stained shirts. Kids were mean. He remembered the anger he'd felt at being dealt a bad hand and how hard he'd had to work to get out of that mess.

With all these thoughts flying through his head he finally said: "Jennifer, I know what it is like to be poor but look at where I am today. I have nothing against people that are poor. But I am against any free hand outs because people are quick to take advantage of them. They are only poor because of themselves! It is not your job to solve their problems."

She waited until her father had driven through the imposing stone gateway of the country estate then pushed her luck with one more statement. **"You are wrong. No one chooses to be born poor!"**

Reuben replied angrily, "Neither did I, but look where I am now." He paused for a few minutes before concluding heavily, "All right, go ahead and make your own decision about your future, but understand that I will not be happy if you join a non-profit organisation."

The reservation for dinner got cancelled and they headed back home. Later, lying on her bed in tears, Jennifer chewed over the conversation. "How can my dad be so heartless? Can't he see how miserable he always is? I don't want that for my life," she muttered.

It was a sleepless night but, in the end, she decided to follow their advice. She would join her mum's practice and see how it went, but if it did not work out, she would quit and follow her passion.

7. The Practice

The first few weeks of working with her mum were not easy, and Jennifer often felt like quitting, but she stuck it out as she had made a commitment to be there for at least six months and she loved seeing patients. Jennifer was an excellent doctor, just like her mum, and it was not long before her reputation resulted in a long waiting list of patients. In the past, Jennifer had lived off her parents' money, but now she was living off her own.

After two years, Jennifer was ready for her next adventure and decided to start her own practice. She figured that she was in the prime of her life, and the non-profit organisation was always something she could take up when she was older. Registering her practice, opening the business account, and getting all the necessary licences, insurance and indemnity cover took quite a while. Her mum found great premises in a busy area for Jennifer, and she took a three-year lease on the property. It cost more than she'd expected to get her rooms ready for business and she ran out of savings, but fortunately her mum and dad were willing to plough in a bit of their own money, and she was incredibly grateful.

On the opening day, she was surprised to see how many people arrived to make an appointment with her. This was due to the excellent reputation she had developed whilst working with her mum. Her first year of business flew by and it was incredibly challenging as there were lots of expenses for equipment and supplies. There was also the cost of advertising and the receptionist's salary. The result of this was that she did not make much of a profit, but all the same she needed to do a tax return. It was a tough job as she had to account for all her income and the expenses related to the practice and would have to pay tax on the profit. She submitted her return online; this was especially stressful as she had misplaced many of the invoices.

Jennifer also met with Peter, her financial consultant, for a full review on her medical malpractice insurance. It was important to have adequate cover as there was always the risk that if something bad happened to a patient, they or their family would take Jennifer to court. Fortunately, Peter reassured her that she had all the necessary cover but pointed out that in her personal capacity she'd overlooked her retirement needs. Jennifer laughed when she heard this.

"I am only in my early thirties! I have lots of time."

"Seriously, the best time to contribute to a fund for your retirement is when you are young," Peter advised.

"Why do I need to think about retirement now? I'm too young to think about that."

"It is great having your own business," Peter replied, "but at some stage you may want to stop working and when you do, what type of lifestyle would you like to lead? By starting contributions early and at a small cost each month, you will have a greater probability of retiring with the financial security you need. However, if you leave it until you are older and closer to retirement age, then you are at greater risk of not having the means to live the lifestyle you want."

When Peter saw that Jennifer could not grasp the concept, he explained that everyone's life is a ticking clock which cannot go backwards. Some people start setting aside money when they have time on their side, and they plan for the day they can no longer work. These are the ones that save in their twenties and have just over forty years to save if they plan to retire in their sixties. Others do not realise that their clock is ticking and as a result only start saving when they are close to retirement.

In most cases, those who start saving in their fifties do not have enough time to save up for their retirement. The realisation causes panic, and they inevitably end up having to work long after they should have retired, or they must rely on the financial support of loved ones.

Peter stated, **"The choice you need to make is whether you want to make plans for your retirement when you are young or face the real possibility of a financial struggle when you are old."**

Once Jennifer admitted that she was interested in the policy, Peter did a full financial assessment of her long-term needs and explained the effect of inflation, where something will cost more in the future than it does right now. So, if she needed a million pounds to retire comfortably in today's terms, she would need far more in twenty years' time, as the purchasing power of her money would be less.

Peter went on to explain that she could manage this risk by linking the amount she saved to inflation. This way her contribution to her retirement policy would increase in line with inflation, and in so doing increase the probability that she had enough to retire on. Jennifer agreed and took out a retirement policy. She also learnt that she would get a tax benefit as this was the government's way of encouraging people to save for their retirement.

Business improved dramatically in the second year and Jennifer hired a bookkeeper as well as a tax consultant to optimise her tax. The practice was running at a healthy profit, and it just kept getting busier, so much so that she could not cope with the many patients who wanted to see her. As a result, she took on two additional doctors to help with the workload. This brought in more money as they had to pay her for the referrals as well as for renting her premises. Jennifer also made her first major investment which was a three-bedroom apartment in London. She paid a seventy percent deposit and planned to pay the remainder off within two years.

Jennifer loved what she did, and it was making her wealthy. Long hours were common and when she did have time to relax, she splashed out on expensive jewellery and branded clothes. On a few occasions she went out partying with her friends and it was great to let her hair down. She was also incredibly generous and always gave to the poor despite her father's view on it. Jennifer was literally printing money, and whenever she took leave, she travelled to exotic locations. She fell in love with a private villa in Majorca which overlooked the sea. It took a while, but she managed to purchase it.

There were many people that wanted to be with her, but she struggled to form long-term relationships. On the few occasions that she did have someone in her life, Jennifer soon got bored and found a reason to end it. One evening, while sitting alone in her bedroom, Jennifer began to weep uncontrollably. The pills she had taken earlier were not helping her mood and she felt herself struggling to breathe. As panic set in, she grabbed her phone.

"Help me mum, I cannot breathe!"

Jennifer's mum panicked: "What has happened Jen? Where are you?"

When she didn't answer, Reuben and Sue raced to Jennifer's apartment hoping that she was there, calling the emergency response service on the way. The paramedics got there first and had to break open the front door when she did not respond to their repeated knocking. They found her unconscious on her bedroom floor. By the time Sue and Reuben arrived, the paramedics had stabilised their daughter and were getting her ready for the ambulance.

That night and the following day, numerous tests were performed to find out what had happened. It was clear that Jennifer had drugs in her system and had suffered a mild overdose. Over and above this she also had suffered an emotional breakdown. When she regained consciousness, she explained that she had taken tablets as she was struggling to sleep because of the pressure at work. She had inadvertently double-dosed when she forgot that she had already taken tablets.

Her doctor disagreed and explained that the blood tests showed 3.4-Methylenedioxymethamphetamine (MDMA) in her blood. This wasn't a once-off event: the results indicated that she had been taking drugs for a while. Being a doctor, she knew instantly what he was talking about and denied that she had taken ecstasy. She insisted that she had only taken calming tablets. Jennifer was in denial. The doctor closed the discussion by advising her that as she was a medical doctor, he was under obligation to report the findings to the General Medical Council and there could be further consequences.

The situation was serious, and Jennifer's parents and doctor recommended that she book herself into a drug rehabilitation centre. This was the best place to get help with her addiction, yet she was having none of it.

8. The Deception

On the day she was discharged from the hospital, her parents gave one final push for her to go to a drug rehabilitation centre, but Jennifer refused as she did not believe she had an addiction. Her mum and dad then insisted that she stay with them for a couple of months, just to help her get back on her feet. Jennifer agreed to that.

The General Medical Practice reviewed Jennifer's case and suspended her licence for a period of three months. There were also conditions that she had to meet which involved regular screenings. Jennifer was grateful for the outcome as it could have been so much worse. The first few weeks were incredibly difficult and although she was doing the right things, her body still craved drugs. She had many sleepless nights and shed lots of tears while her parents did their best to hold things together.

By the fourth month things started to get easier and the cravings were almost completely gone. Jennifer felt that she was ready to make the move back to her own apartment. This would coincide with returning to work as she had passed all the screenings and her suspension had been lifted. Her mum and dad were supportive, but on one condition: they would visit her every day for the first few weeks. This was their way of checking up on Jennifer to make sure that she kept on the straight and narrow. Jennifer agreed to everything and thanked them for how good they had been to her. She reassured them that she would be ok.

On the day she left her parents' house she fizzed with nervous energy as she was excited about the prospect of living on her own again. When she walked into her home it was surprisingly clean. Her mum helped her settle in and left about an hour later. Jennifer watched as the car drove down the road and out of sight, then she started searching. Before long there were cups, sauces, and plates all over the counter, and she upended her linen cupboard as she grew increasingly frustrated. Soon it looked as if she had been burgled and it suddenly dawned on her why her apartment was so clean. Her parents must have arranged for cleaners to do a deep clean to find all the drugs she had hidden.

The cravings grew stronger and after Jennifer had tidied up the apartment and put everything back where it belonged, she called a few friends. That night she went out and partied until the early hours of the morning. She could hardly walk as she had drunk way too much, but fortunately the taxi driver made sure that she got home safely. The next morning, she had a massive headache, and called her receptionist to say that she was delaying her return to work by another week as she needed time to settle into her home. Betty was excellent at her job, and she assured Jennifer that she would rearrange the appointments that had already been scheduled.

Betty asked if she needed help with anything. Jennifer politely declined and hung up, then called her mum and had a chat about how things were going. Sue wanted to see her, but Jennifer said she was quite busy and asked if it were okay if she came over the next day instead. Her mum agreed and was happy that things were going well for her daughter. That night Jennifer had an even bigger party, and a few friends slept over.

Jennifer had no idea how much money she was spending and neither did she care. Over the next few weeks, she played an immensely enjoyable juggling game. She was good at hiding what was going on and she knew that eventually her mum would stop coming over. All Jennifer needed was a little time and then she could be free. The moment came after the sixth week.

"Hi Jen, is it okay if we skip this week?" her mum said one morning on the phone.

Jennifer tried her best not to sound too eager. "Why? What has happened?"

"Dad and I thought that as you are doing so well, we would go away for a week's holiday."

This was music to her ears. "Sure mum. I'm glad everything is ok. I will be fine, but one week does not sound long enough. I hope you are not cutting it short because of me?"

Her mum replied, "No sweety, of course not."

Jennifer knew that her mum was not telling the truth and in the most diplomatic way possible she said, "Mum, you and dad have done so much for me, and I know that it has not been easy for either of you. You both deserve more than a break; you deserve a medal. I want to pay for your holiday, and I insist that you take two weeks. I won't take no for an answer."

Sue tried to refuse but Jennifer insisted. The holiday was finalised, although her dad was annoyed because he had more than enough money and it was not right that his daughter should pay for it.

While her parents were on holiday, Jennifer found even more freedom and started purchasing enormous quantities of drugs from a dealer a friend had introduced her to. The addictions she had had in the past returned with greater intensity and she struggled to keep up with her cravings.

Her mum and dad called her a few times after they got back from holiday, and she always steered the conversation towards them and their lives. Not long after that, while on a night out, the same friend that had introduced Jennifer to ecstasy finally convinced her to try cocaine. She could not say no and soon became addicted. The cost was immense, but Jennifer had more than enough savings to cover it. The partying got even more intense and there were many people that were only too happy to follow Jennifer around; after all, she was paying for everything. Yet the limitless supply of money was starting to dry up.

She had blown over fifty thousand pounds and now had no choice but to sell her holiday home to support her drug addiction.

The days rolled into weeks and the weeks rolled into months but for Jennifer every day felt the same, she needed her fix. Her addiction was having an impact on her ability to perform at work and some of her patients moved their business to other doctors as she often cancelled appointments at the last minute.

Jennifer's mum could see that something was not right, but every time Sue broached the subject, she was subjected to verbal abuse and told plainly to stay out of her daughter's business. Her dad tried to intervene, and he too was stonewalled. There was nothing they could do. Jennifer cut them out of her life and at the same time told Betty that she was taking a six-month sabbatical. Betty was to transfer all her appointments to the other doctors that operated from her premises. She also told Betty that she had cancelled her retirement policy and asked her to make sure that Peter, her financial consultant, was aware of this.

Betty agreed but sounded concerned, so Jennifer assured her that she was only cancelling the policy as she had more than enough money to live on, not that it was any of Betty's business. Jennifer then called both her bookkeeper and tax consultant and informed them that their services were no longer required.

She sold her home in London and found a flat to rent. The money from the sale enabled her to travel to Menorca and she paid for three of her best friends to join her. Jennifer was literally burning her money, but that didn't bother her in the least.

Once the money was gone, they all headed back to London. All she cared about was having her daily fix. Jennifer had no choice but to sell her practice as she needed the money. The other doctors who operated from her premises were extremely happy to purchase the practice and they took over her lease agreement. The price they gave her was small in relation to how much it was worth, but she did not care. They also hired Betty as she had given them so much work while Jennifer was on her sabbatical, and they knew she was excellent at her job. Jennifer's life was spiralling out of control. The money she made from the sale disappeared just like all the other cash. To sustain her habit, she kept on selling things and eventually everything was gone, she had nothing left.

She approached a few 'friends' for money and it was painful to experience their rejection. She had spent thousands of pounds on them, yet they were not willing to part with a penny. Jennifer was eventually evicted from her rented property. Despite having nowhere to live, she refused to call her parents; she had lost all self-respect and had taken to being homeless. On the first night of sleeping on the streets she was assaulted. It was a horrendous experience, and she was covered in bruises and shame. Every night she looked for an alley that was well-lit, and she kept a large metal pole close to her side, but that did not stop the beatings. Jennifer's life was a mess and there seemed to be no way out. She contemplated ending it, but something inside of her pushed back.

9. The Recovery

Late one night Sue was lying awake worrying about Jennifer when she heard a soft knocking sound and immediately nudged Reuben: "Wake up! Someone is at the front door."

Half asleep he quickly responded, "Rubbish, I can't hear anything."

"Go check, there is someone knocking on our door."

Reuben knew that Sue was not going to take no for an answer. He sighed as he made his way down the stairs. Sue had a knack of waking him up at all hours of the night whenever she heard a strange sound, and it always amounted to nothing. When Reuben finally got to the front door, he did hear someone knocking, which caused the hair on the back of his neck to rise as he was in fear. He looked through a small side window to see who it was. The person standing there was unrecognisable.

"What do you want?" he shouted.

"Daddy it is me," Jennifer sobbed.

Ruben opened the door quickly and wept as he reached out to hug her. His daughter was home.

Her mum recognised her voice and raced downstairs, almost falling as she flung her arms around Jennifer. She did not look well and was extremely thin. Jennifer sobbed as she explained how she had ruined her life and had nowhere else to go. Her parents continued to hug her tightly and reassured her that she was home. Over the next few days Jennifer agreed that she needed to see a professional as she was addicted to drugs and wanted to get her life right. Her mum phoned every drug rehabilitation centre available and booked her into a highly rated one. The first few days were the worst—she felt vulnerable, and the cravings drove her mad. Her emotions went from the height of aggression to the depths of despair, and she often wanted to run away. She found it difficult to comprehend how she had fallen so far, and she had so much regret.

The centre was quite different to what she'd expected; it was nothing like the movies she'd seen. **She found solace in the fact that she was not the only one struggling to get free, as there were many others there who were going through the same experience.** The cravings continued to feel like needles digging into her soul, causing her to cry out for another fix.

Every day in her support group discussions she would ask if the cravings would ever go away, but the difficult answer was always the same. They would not stop, but their intensity would decrease, and she would have the tools to deal with them. During the process of recovery Jennifer spent a few months in and out of rehab. She had two sponsors: one would call her in the morning and the other at night. They did this to ensure that they could be there for her and help her through her struggles. It was a long hard road, but she finally got free. She closed her Instagram account and ended the friendships that she knew were dangerous for her, because there was no going back. Financially her parents were there for her, and they paid for all her expenses. Jennifer could not work as her medical licence had been suspended once again.

On the three-hundred-and-seventy-eighth day of being drug and alcohol free, Jennifer decided she wanted to go back to work. There was a job available as an assistant to the resident doctor at a drug rehabilitation centre and Jennifer applied. She was a little apprehensive in the interview but came across very well and they offered her the job. The interviewers liked the fact that she had been a great doctor in the past, and that she had first-hand experience in what they were dealing with at the centre. The pay was not the best, but Jennifer did not care, she really wanted the job. The centre had a retirement scheme for their employees and asked if Jennifer had an existing policy that she wanted to transfer to it. Jennifer recalled that she used to have one but had cancelled it years ago, so she was not sure whether she had cover. That week she contacted Peter her financial consultant who was so surprised to hear from her. Jennifer learnt that although she had cancelled the retirement policy, she still had the funds that she had paid in, as she could only access them on retirement. This was great news and she arranged to have them transferred to the centre's retirement scheme.

The first few weeks at the centre went better than expected and the doctor she was assisting agreed to help her regain her medical licence. It was going to be a lengthy process as the General Medical Council had imposed extremely strict conditions that needed to be met before they would reconsider her case. Jennifer's work was excellent, and she was helping many young people overcome their addictions. They all loved her and often said that she was the first doctor they had ever met who really understood the pain they were going through. Jennifer always put them right by saying that she was no longer a practicing medical doctor but rather just an assistant. However, she was close to regaining her licence to practice under supervision and hoped it would happen sooner rather than later.

After two years at the rehabilitation centre, Jennifer regained her medical licence in full. By now she was a regular speaker at secondary schools and whenever she spoke to the students, she always shared her story. She would start by introducing herself as a qualified medical doctor who had graduated at Oxford University. She would then go on to explain that in the past she'd had a successful medical practice, a paid-off property in London, a holiday home, luxury cars, expensive jewellery, and a wardrobe full of designer clothes, but she had lost all of it.

"You probably want to know how this happened; how did I lose everything?" she would ask her young audience.

After a long pause, she would explain that having a successful practice came at a cost, she was always under tremendous work pressure. To cope with it, she started taking calming tablets. At the same time, she went out every weekend with friends partying at various clubs. This lifestyle worked for her for a few months, but then she made a mistake. She'd had an unbelievably bad week, as a young patient had died. In her distraught state, another partygoer offered her an ecstasy tablet which was guaranteed to make her feel better. This was not the first time she was offered ecstasy and as a medical doctor she knew better than to take it, but that night she did. It was her first experience with a hard drug, and she enjoyed the immediate effect, but the next morning she woke with an excruciating headache. In that moment she decided this was the first and last time she would ever take the drug. A week later she was out again with the same friends, and she took another ecstasy tablet. **The once-off experience with an illicit drug quickly escalated into an addiction.** Every weekend she promised herself that this would be the last time, but it never was.

As Jennifer told her story, everyone listened attentively, trying to imagine how a doctor could get caught up in this. She went on to explain that after one late night out, while still high on ecstasy, she accidently overdosed by taking headache tablets and her calming tablets as well. When in hospital the doctor seeing her warned that she had an addiction, but she refused to believe it.

She was in denial; she thought she had everything under control and could stop whenever she wanted. A few months after the mild overdose she'd moved onto cocaine and that was her point of no return. Using her medical training, she described in detail what had happened inside her body at the time. Her physiological state was changing, and she was no longer in control as her body's intense craving for drugs now ruled her life. However, drugs are not free, nor are they cheap. The cravings were so bad that she did whatever she could to get her next fix. She sold everything she owned, and the drug dealers were only too happy to take every penny in exchange for drugs.

At that time, she didn't want her parents' help; she cared nothing for them and had no self-respect. She ended up being homeless, and her friends, on whom she had spent so much of her money, had vanished. She was alone. Jennifer told her audiences of the physical and sexual abuse she'd experienced on the streets. The details made them wince in disbelief. Her story continued: she'd been to hell and back and wanted to end it all, but something stopped her. Standing on the precipice of life and death, at three a.m. in the morning, she knocked on the door of her parents' home. This was the starting point of her recovery: she accepted that she was an addict and wanted to change even though she had no idea how. Jennifer spoke about the drug rehabilitation centre, the support groups, and her relapses. The struggle was immense, but she got through it like so many before her. As a result of her addiction her medical licence had been suspended. Even though she was now off drugs, she could not work as a doctor. She made sure the audience knew how many years it had taken—not to mention the rigorous requirements she had to meet— before she could practice again. Getting her licence back had been another miracle.

To conclude, Jennifer made it clear that no one was immune to addiction, not even a doctor. She told them that there were people of their own age at the drug rehabilitation centre, and when she counselled them, it was always clear that they'd never believed that they would ever become an addict; they were just having some fun.

"Drugs are not fun, they are a poison that has the potential to destroy not only your body, but every part of your life," she said to the hushed audience.

Jennifer went into detail about the many lives she had seen get free from drugs, and how the group continued to support each other through weekly meetings and phone calls. The cravings would never go away completely, but they had each other and the tools to deal with them. She spoke with honesty, not to scare people but to warn them of the real dangers associated with drugs. Her messages always ended on a positive note: every addict had the potential to get free, but the person in the best position was the one who never tried drugs at all. The passion and authenticity with which she spoke kept the audience engaged from start to finish, and when her speech ended, she always received a standing ovation.

Jennifer had found the meaningful life she had so craved when she was younger, and her open and candid story touched and saved countless lives.

10. Emmanuel's Journey

Emmanuel spent the day looking over his shoulder, convinced that Jason would attack him at any moment. Earlier, the rush of adrenaline had made him feel invincible but within a fairly short time that had drained away, leaving him tense and afraid. *I cannot believe I stood up to Jason. What was I thinking?* The world around Emmanuel had disappeared. All he could think of was that Jason would beat him up—not if, but when. At the final bell, Emmanuel bolted out the classroom and into the street. He ran and kept on running. After three miles, he stopped to catch his breath, completely exhausted. He looked back slowly and saw someone approaching. Fortunately, it was just an old man.

"Are you ok?" the man asked as he drew level.

"Yes, I'm fine thanks," Emmanuel said automatically, wiping his sweaty forehead.

The stranger then asked, "What are you running from, young man? Who frightened you?"

Emmanuel had to end this conversation fast in case Jason caught up with him.

"Just running late, thanks again for your concern, must go," he said as he launched into a slow jog towards his home.

When he reached the front door, he let himself in quickly and headed for the kitchen, where he poured a large glass of water. His school clothes were soaked with sweat, and he pulled off his jacket and tie and threw them on a chair before dropping onto the old couch.

The door opened and his sister Beth peered around it nervously.

"Emmanuel, you scared me! What are you doing home so soon?" she said, advancing into the room.

He almost laughed at the sight of his sister holding a cricket bat in her hand. "Sorry I scared you. I ran home from school today and that's why I got back early."

She was not convinced. "Why did you run?"

He glared at her in annoyance. "It is none of your business," he said and went up to the bedroom which he shared with his two older brothers. Fortunately, they were both still at work.

Up until three years ago, the family had lived in a nice house and Emmanuel had his own room. That was until Jacob, his older brother, convinced Simon, their dad, to sign surety for a loan he needed for his start-up company's expansion plans. Their father had been a successful businessman who had retired at sixty with a healthy amount of savings and a great pension, and he thought nothing of signing surety for the loan. It was just a formality.

Jacob's company did far worse than expected and he declared bankruptcy as a result the bank demanded payment from his dad as he had signed surety for the loan. Simon tried to fight them, but all that did was cost him money in legal fees. In the end there was no choice but to pay up. The family's five-bedroom property was sold and the proceeds, together with all his savings, had to be used to settle the debt. Simon had to go back to work because his pension was not enough to cover all their expenses. It had been an extremely hard lesson and Simon vowed to never stand surety for anyone again.

Emmanuel could not understand why his dad was not angry with his brother Jacob. Whenever the subject came up, his father would always say the same thing: "God has a plan, even if we don't understand it."

Every night the entire family ate together around the dinner table. They always laid a place in front of an empty seat to remember their mum who had passed away a few years earlier.

"How was your day?" Simon would ask each of them in turn and they would have to describe how their day had unfolded; this was a tradition they had followed from as far back as Emmanuel could remember.

That evening, when it was his turn to speak, he avoided saying much as he did not want to relive the trauma or get his older brothers involved.

"All good, dad."

Beth at once challenged him: "That is not true Emmanuel! Tell dad why you ran home today."

He glared at Beth.

"Why *did* you run home, Emmanuel?" his father asked with interest.

There was no escape, so for the next ten minutes he shared the details of all that had happened that day. Jacob and James seethed with anger towards Jason, but Simon smiled hugely.

"I am proud of you my son, well done for standing up to that bully."

His brothers wanted to know where Jason lived. Emmanuel pleaded with them to not get involved as it was his problem, not theirs. Their father agreed and told them to stay out of it.

Emmanuel felt better after speaking about what had happened as it released a great deal of tension.

The dinner discussion soon moved on to his future. This was his last year of school and he had already told his father that he wanted to go to university and study accountancy. A few months earlier he'd sent off applications to every available university, but they all turned him down as he did not have enough points to meet the minimum criteria. He was not a top student and no matter how hard he tried (and he really did try hard) he would always end up in the mid- to lower tier of his class. In desperation, Emmanuel applied at foreign universities. One of these had now given him provisional approval, but they requested the fees upfront. The dinner table discussion ended after Simon agreed to take Emmanuel to the bank and ask for a loan to pay for the studies.

A few days later, Emmanuel and his father met with a friendly and extremely knowledgeable bank consultant named Anna. When she heard that the money was needed to fund overseas studies for Emmanuel, she told them about the various options and Simon decided to apply for a personal loan.

Emmanuel had butterflies in his stomach, as it looked like his father would get the loan. Anna stared at her computer screen as her fingers sped over the keys. But, after a few minutes, she told them that the application had been declined. Emmanuel's world came crashing down. His disappointment was palpable.

"Why can't you help?" Simon demanded desperately.

Anna responded, "Unfortunately the system has declined the loan, based on what you can afford to pay back."

"But I have banked with you for over forty years—doesn't that count for anything?"

Anna empathised with Simon that the news was not what he wanted to hear but said the bank was legally bound to adhere to the regulations, and he could not afford the loan.

Sitting there listening to the conversation, tears welled up in Emmanuel's eyes. It was so unfair. His dad had paid for both his older brothers' studies and now he was suffering for Jacob's mistake. Emmanuel walked out of the bank feeling devastated. *Life was not fair! Why hadn't he been born into a family like Jennifer's where there was so much wealth?*

Over the next few months, the combination of bitterness towards his brother and his disappointment in not being able to go to university was a fatal mixture and, without even realising it, he slid into depression.

Emmanuel's normal happy personality was doused with sadness and each afternoon when he got home from school, he went straight to his room to huddle in his bed and sleep away his pain. He stopped talking to his friends, and negative thoughts tormented him day and night.

When the school year finally finished, Emmanuel spent a couple of days doing absolutely nothing. He barely got out of bed and his dad was very worried.

During an evening meal, Simon asked, "When will you start looking for a job?"

"I can't see any jobs I like."

"Beggars cannot be choosers, son."

Emmanuel shouted back, "I am not a beggar!" and got up and left the table.

Before he even reached his bedroom door, his dad grabbed his arm. "Do not speak to me like that! What has got into you?"

Emmanuel knew he had crossed the line. "Sorry dad, I'm just really upset that I can't go to university."

"Son, when I was younger, I also did not go to university, but I worked hard and have raised four beautiful children. Your mum would be turning in her grave to see you speaking to me this way. You've always been the positive one in this family."

Emmanuel stood there without a word.

He had never seen his dad so angry, but even the anger could not get through the dark cloud that consumed him.

The next day Emmanuel got out of bed at one-thirty in the afternoon. He turned on his laptop and started searching for jobs. His search was based on the salary he wanted, but he soon realised that his skills did not meet the employers' requirements. He broadened his search parameters and found jobs at local restaurants, where no experience was necessary, and applied for a few of them. Within a week of applying, he was called for an interview at a local restaurant; this went well, and they offered him a job as a waiter. The hours were reasonable and, after agreeing on a start date, they arranged for a work uniform to be delivered to his house as everyone who worked at the restaurant had to wear a uniform—it was part of their brand. The first day of work arrived and his depression almost kept him in bed, but his dad was on hand to make sure he left on time. The day went quite quickly and provided a much-needed distraction, but on the way home tears welled up as his despair resurfaced. He was struggling to cope with the disappointment of where life had taken him.

Simon could see that his boy was not happy, so he invited him out for brunch on Sunday. They ordered Emmanuel's favourite breakfast of bacon, eggs, tomato, and sausages. Afterwards, they watched a film at the local cinema. Emmanuel was having a wonderful day with his dad, and it got even better when they went to a local coffee shop where he ordered a slice of double chocolate cake.

It was here that his dad broached the difficult subject.

"Emmanuel, how are you, my boy?"

"I am feeling great, dad. It has been an awesome day."

"No, my boy, how are you *really* feeling, not just today but in general?"

"I am fine dad."

When his dad repeated the question a third time in a voice filled with empathy, Emmanuel dropped his defences.

"Actually dad, I feel depressed. I don't know how to shake it off."

"What are you depressed about?"

"I feel cheated by Jacob and at the same time I feel terrible about how much I resent him for robbing you of your money, and I really don't like working at the restaurant. I feel like I don't belong there."

In a perfect world, his dad would have had a solution, but this was life, and his dad had no answers. Simon could only reassure Emmanuel that he was a great brother and a fantastic son and that he loved him.

11. The Gamer

After a few months of working at the restaurant, Emmanuel tried finding another job but was not successful. He grew increasingly frustrated at work and concluded that the restaurant business was not for him, so he quit his job. At the time his dad tried to get him to reconsider, but Emmanuel was having none of it, and instead spent the money he had saved to set himself up with some top of the range gaming equipment.

Being unemployed gave him a lot of free time, and he filled it by playing online games. He enjoyed the surge of adrenaline he felt when winning, and he was also making so many friends along the way. Sputnick123 was an excellent fighter and had a wicked sense of humour; GIGI777 was super rich and had all the gear anyone could ever ask for and was always generous; GeoffTheDude was equally loaded and was the best player with whom he had ever played. The four of them became a tactical unit that was incredibly hard to beat. Every day they planned to meet and like clockwork they never let each other down. Although

Emmanuel had no idea where his teammates lived, how old they were, or had ever met any of them in real life, they were now his clan.

After two months of this, Emmanuel's dad finally lost his temper and stormed into the bedroom.

"This is enough! I am tired of you living in your bedroom, and I refuse to support you financially while you're perfectly capable of working. What have you been doing all day?"

Emmanuel replied, "Looking for a job, dad!"

His father interrupted him: "Looking for a job? How? What job have you applied for?"

"I have applied for many."

"Show me! Show me where you applied for a job," Simon said sceptically.

Emmanuel was unable to show him any recent applications, as the last job he'd applied for had been five weeks earlier.

"What have you been doing?" his dad repeated.

Emmanuel was silent.

"Emmanuel, I am sick and tired of you spending the entire day on the internet playing games instead of looking for a job. I am changing the password and you will not have internet access anymore."

"Great! So, how am I supposed to look for a job?"

Simon snapped back, "You can look for jobs in the evening using my computer, and during the day you can walk into town and go from shop to shop asking them if they have any jobs available. I don't care how you do it, just get a job!"

Two weeks later Emmanuel found a job at a local supermarket, and this was merely a means to an end, as he wanted the internet back. There was no small amount of apologising to his gaming clan who were upset that he had let them down. They were reluctant to take him back as in his absence they had taken on a new gamer, Flick123. The first month at the new job went by quite quickly, but after a few days Emmanuel found himself arriving at work later and later. The manager gave him a dressing-down, but it made no difference. Finally, Emmanuel lost his job. Each morning he dressed, left the house then returned once his dad had left for work. After a few weeks of doing this, his dad found out. He was furious!

Emmanuel lost his internet privilege again and, if it were not for his sister's intervention, he would've been on the street. This started off a new cycle. As regular as a tango, Emmanuel would get a job, get the internet back, quit or get fired then lose the internet again. His dad spoke to friends and family as he had run out of ideas on what to do. They suggested that he tell Emmanuel that he was to find his own accommodation, but his father had too much love and guilt to do what they suggested.

As the years passed, Emmanuel went in and out of relationships. The women in his life wanted him to work and make money and he was not having any of it; they would support him for a while, but inevitably all moved on. His love life closely resembled his work life, always a starter but never a finisher. The turning point in his life came when GIGI777, the final gamer in his team, called it a day. The rest of the clan had moved on many months back.

Sitting in his room alone as a twenty-eight-year-old was depressing. His father hardly spoke to him. Emmanuel finally realized that every time he got a job, he found a way to lose it. He knew he had to change but really didn't want to go back to supermarkets or restaurants. He called GIGI777 and took a risk in sharing his predicament as he needed advice.

GIGI777 was surprised to hear from him and after a quick catch-up, Emmanuel poured out his heart. She was a good listener and was brutely honest with him.

"Emmanuel you're not thinking straight. Why not start your own business?"

"I don't know if I can do it," he replied.

Gigi ignored this and talked about the businesses her family ran and encouraged him to give it a go. He knew Gigi was right.

"What business should I start?"

"Start with something you enjoy doing," was her simple reply.

Emmanuel thanked GiGi and hung up. He was pleased he had called her and was excited at the prospect of starting a business.

12. The Failure

When Emmanuel thought of what he enjoyed doing, two hobbies stood out. He loved taking pictures so maybe a photography business, or he could start a garden service because he found it relaxing to mow his dad's lawn. In the end he decided on a photography business as it seemed an easier option.

He searched the internet to see what professional photographers charged and it looked promising. He also watched a few YouTube videos on photography which mentioned lighting, apertures, and aspect ratios, not to mention the vast array of lenses he could use. It all seemed terribly complicated. The cost of a new camera was more than he could afford. His own camera, which his father had given to him as a birthday present, was roughly ten years old. It didn't have a zoom lens, so he'd have to stand quite close to the person he was photographing, but he was optimistic that he could make this work.

While researching how to start a company he read about the importance of a business plan and decided to write his own. His plan was very simple: he would target his family, his friends and then his local neighbourhood. Once he was established, he would upgrade his equipment and set up a website. Everything sounded great and now all he needed was some paying customers.

He was unsure how much to charge but had seen a photo booth in his local store where customers were charged six pounds to get six photos. Using this price as a guide, he worked out that he could charge twenty pounds for the same service as he would go to their homes rather than them having to travel to the local store.

When his dad initially heard about the idea, he wasn't sure whether starting a photography business was the right thing for Emmanuel, but it was certainly better than him sitting in his room doing nothing. He asked some questions, and his son had an answer for everything; he even had a sales pitch which sounded very convincing, so much so that Simon agreed to be his son's first paying customer—even though he did not need a photograph of himself.

Emmanuel charged his dad twenty pounds and got him to pay the money upfront. Then he took the picture, but when looking at the lcd screen on his camera, it was out of focus, so he took another one and this was also out of focus. Emmanuel could not understand why his photographs were so fuzzy. He went to the bathroom and used some toilet paper to clean the lens, then took another photo. It helped a little but not enough as the picture quality still wasn't great. He then did some research on Google to find out what was happening. Someone recommended a cleaning product for the lens as well as a special cloth; it would cost eight pounds and ninety-nine pence for both including delivery, but this was a worthwhile investment, he felt, and he used part of the twenty pounds his dad had paid him to purchase it. A day later the goods arrived, and Emmanuel was back in business. He tried to convince his dad to pay another twenty pounds for the photoshoot as it was not his fault that the lens had been dirty, but his dad refused. *It is ok,* Emmanuel thought, *I will do this one for free because it is for my dad.* The images looked much better: they were sharp and clear.

He showed his dad the small LCD display on his camera and said, "Here's your picture dad, what do you think?"

"It looks great son. When do I get it?"

"What do you mean?"

"When do I get my photograph?"

"Don't worry dad, I will email it to you."

"Email?" his dad blustered. "I don't want an email; I want the photograph I paid for so that I can put it into a frame!"

"Oh ok, but that is going to cost another five pounds."

"Why another five pounds?"

"The quote I gave you was for a digital photograph, not a printed photograph."

His dad reluctantly agreed to pay the extra five pounds and Emmanuel headed off to town to the printing machine he had seen next to the photo booth. A standard four-by-six photograph cost two pounds to print.

Emmanuel printed the photograph, but it was not clear, so he logged a complaint with the store manager, who assessed the machine and found nothing wrong with it.

"The fault," he said, "lies with your camera."

This was not good news at all, and Emmanuel reluctantly headed off home and gave the photograph to his dad.

"Thanks Emmanuel. This is a great photograph," his dad said unenthusiastically.

Emmanuel decided to press on with his business despite the camera's faults. He called his extended family members but one by one they declined his offer as they had no need for a twenty-pound photograph. One of his cousins came close to paying to have her photograph taken, but once she saw the one his dad had paid for, she changed her mind. Emmanuel decided to move onto friends in the hope that they would be more accommodating, but this was fruitless as well.

Emmanuel wasn't one to give up on a promising idea, so he launched phase three. His plan was to do door-to-door sales in his local neighbourhood, as he did not have any money for advertising. The first day his timing was all wrong as everyone was at work. The next day he decided he would go door-to-door in the early evening. It was surprising how many people did not answer their door even though they were home, and for those that did answer, they simply told him to go away as they did not need a photo.

Then there were those that seemed desperately lonely, and although these people spent ages chatting to him, he knew they had no intention of ever having their photograph taken.

Finally, he knocked on a door where a couple agreed to do a photoshoot. He initially tried to charge forty pounds as there were two of them, but when they refused, he agreed to only charge them twenty pounds.

After two weeks of canvassing, Emmanuel had only made sixty pounds and he was exhausted. He had covered most of the houses in his neighbourhood and the clients he had taken photos of were not impressed with the quality of his work. One woman was so scathing that she told Emmanuel to keep the photograph and sarcastically advised him to use it as a reference for other customers; it was her gift to him.

Photography was far more complicated than he had initially thought, and although he loved speaking to potential customers and had a great sales pitch, he realised that it wasn't for him, so he closed the business.

13. The Success

Although his first venture had failed, Emmanuel realised he loved being his own boss. He was good at canvassing and had built up a good business network, despite not selling many photographs. It was time to start his garden service and he was sure it would succeed, it just had to. He told his dad about this idea, and asked if he could borrow his garden equipment to start his business. After much debating Simon reluctantly agreed to the request and once again became his son's first paying customer. He paid fifteen pounds to get his lawn mown.

Emmanuel had figured that it would only take him thirty minutes to get the job done, but when he tried to start the lawnmower, it would not work. Over an hour passed before he went back to his dad and said despondently, "The lawnmower is broken."

"No, it's not, I used it a month ago, have you read the instructions on the handle?"

"I put the throttle in 'start' position, then I turned the fuel lever to 'on,' then I pulled the chord, but nothing happened."

"Did you check whether there was fuel in the lawnmower?"

"No, where do I check the fuel?"

They went outside to the lawnmower and his dad showed him how to check; not surprisingly, the tank was empty. His dad gave him a five-litre canister and drove him to the service station. The fuel cost seven pounds and Emmanuel tried to get his dad to pay at least half of the fuel as he was cutting *his* lawn, but Simon was having none of it.

Mowing the lawn was surprisingly enjoyable and Emmanuel was good at it. He was a perfectionist and worked hard, and in the end the grass looked amazing. He started taking out the weeds in the lawn and then moved on to the flower beds, something his dad had not paid him to do, but as he was enjoying himself, he decided to do it for free. He trimmed back the plants, removed some that were too close together, and forked over and watered the dry ground. Everything he touched seemed to turn into something magical. A few hours passed and yet he was not even aware of it until his dad called him in for dinner. When his dad saw the garden, he was astounded. In all the years of living at the house, the garden had never looked so beautiful.

That night Emmanuel developed a business plan. He would approach every house in the neighbourhood whose garden looked like it needed some work; he would charge twenty-five pounds for a full service which included flower beds and fifteen pounds for a half service, which was for mowing the lawn only. In the first week he managed to gain ten new customers in his neighbourhood and made one hundred and ninety pounds. The only cost he had was for fuel, which was eighteen pounds, so he made a healthy profit of one hundred and seventy-two pounds.

But the following week was a different story. He was merrily going about his business when suddenly the main window next to the lawn he was mowing shattered into a thousand pieces. The owner raced outside to see what had happened. Emmanuel knew nothing about it, yet there on the living room floor was a stone. The lawnmower had picked it up and flung it straight through the window.

Emmanuel had no insurance, so the owner claimed through his home insurance and made Emmanuel pay for the excess, which was one hundred and fifty pounds. It was a tough lesson as this used up most of his profit. Emmanuel told his dad he wanted to give up on the business. Simon disagreed and encouraged him to keep going as he knew that Emmanuel was good at this, besides he could always get insurance to protect himself from similar situations.

Emmanuel did an internet search and made a couple of calls and sure enough, his dad was right; there was a company that offered a garden insurance policy for businesses just like his. The insurance included public liability which, if he'd taken it out before the accident, would have paid for the window replacement. The policy also included professional indemnity insurance which would cover him if something went wrong with the work he did, and lastly it covered him for employer's liability. This meant that if any of his employees got sick or injured while working for him and they decided to lay a claim against his company, his insurance would cover him for any legal or compensation costs.

Emmanuel had no one working for him at the time, but he knew that at some stage he would need to hire an assistant, so having this cover made sense to him. He registered his business as a sole proprietor and opened a business account. Keeping this account separate from his personal account would help him to complete his annual tax returns more quickly. **He only knew to do this because one of his loyal customers had explained that it was especially important to have separate personal and business bank accounts.**

Emmanuel saved every penny he made. The plan was to use the funds to upgrade his equipment and get a single cab pickup truck for the business. There were many times that he was tempted to take a loan, but he always resisted as he remembered how his brother's debt had wiped out his dad's savings. Besides, if he did take a loan, he would have to pay the bank interest and charges, which would eat into his profits. His resilience paid off and after the first year of operation he had saved enough money to get what he wanted. Emmanuel felt exhilarated and dumfounded at the same time, amazed that his small savings had grown to such an extent that he could now afford to buy a work vehicle with cash.

He could not afford a brand-new vehicle, but none the less he was still buying one with his own money. He paid two thousand and fifty pounds for a used 2002 Hilux, and the remaining six hundred and ninety-three pounds of his savings he used for four brand-new lawnmowers and other garden equipment. **Emmanuel had learnt a valuable lesson: no matter how small your savings are, if you are persistent and diligent, they will grow into a large amount over time.**

Emmanuel was ready to hire assistants, and he decided that he needed three people. He placed an advert in the local paper advertising the jobs for his garden business, no experience needed. The interviews went well, and he hired two students to work over the weekends and two full-time workers who would work during the week. He took on one more person than he had intended, but all four candidates were excellent, and he knew that he could find enough work to keep them busy. The business was growing and so were his savings. Emmanuel also decided that his next goal was to save enough money to buy a flat as he could not live with his dad indefinitely.

After looking around for a while he discovered that he needed a minimum of ten percent deposit if he were to buy a property. Emmanuel worked out that it would take him two years to save up the necessary ten thousand pounds. His savings grew quickly and within no time he had five thousand, one hundred and thirty pounds in his account. This prompted a call from a financial consultant at the bank where his personal account was held. It turned out that when he had opened his account, he had ticked yes to marketing. This explained how the consultant, Abigail, had his contact details. She asked him a few questions about his savings and what he was planning to do with them. He explained his dream of purchasing a flat.

Abigail then asked, "Do you know what interest rate the bank is giving you for the money in your account?"

Emmanuel said, "I don't know."

Abigail responded, "It is not much as you have a basic account, you could be earning a lot more. Would you like to set up an appointment with me to discuss this further?"

Emmanuel replied, "Yes."

The meeting took place at the bank a week later, and Abigail explained more about the account where he presently held his funds, so that he could understand why he was earning such a small amount of interest. To understand Emmanuel's financial needs, she scrutinised his financial history, his long-term goals, and his personal financial situation. She also looked at his appetite for risk. Abigail asked so many questions that Emmanuel felt exhausted. She said she would share her findings at the next appointment as she needed time to look over all the information.

The week went by quickly and Emmanuel finally got to hear Abigail's feedback. She disclosed a whole lot of personal information about him—it was as if she was describing his inner thoughts. It appeared that he was willing to take risks to grow his wealth but, at the same time, he always made sure that he had a backup plan. This was to ensure that he was never in a situation where he had to rely on anyone else for support. Abigail explained that his money was currently very low risk and, although this meant that it was safe and he was unlikely to lose it, at the same time he was getting no interest, so his money wasn't growing; this was called 'low return.' Abigail raised the concern that inflation was currently at a rate of three-point one percent, which meant that the purchase value of his five thousand, one hundred and thirty pounds would be worth three-point one percent less than that in a year's time.

Emmanuel did not understand. "How would it be worth less?" he asked.

"Emmanuel, every year the cost of goods goes up because of inflation. This means that the house you want to purchase today for one hundred thousand pounds is likely to cost you more in a year's time. In the same way, it's unlikely that those goods you purchase for five thousand, one hundred and thirty pounds today will cost the same in a year's time. So, by not earning interest you are in fact losing money, as the purchase value of your money today is most likely to be less in a year's time."

Emmanuel thought for a moment and then asked, "What can I do about this?"

"To keep up with inflation you need to find an investment that gives you at least a 3.1% return."

Emmanuel found her words confusing, but he did understand that he needed to earn interest on his savings.

Abigail went on to explain the benefits of having an Individual Savings Accounts (ISA): **Emmanuel was intrigued to see that when his money grew in the Individual Savings Account (ISA), he would not have to pay tax on the value it grew by.** He also liked the reasonably low risk which seemed ideal for his savings. At that point he was ready to sign as he wanted the ISA, but

Abigail wasn't finished. She explained that publicly listed companies have their shares on the stock market, and when someone buys these shares, they become a shareholder of the company. If this company does well, then the demand for the shares grows. This demand drives up the price of these shares, and the shareholder will make a profit if they should choose to sell. Also, when the company publishes their annual financial report, they will usually declare dividends if they have done well: this means that the company distributes some of its profits to all the shareholders. In this way Emmanuel would make money even without selling shares. Abigail said that although all investments carry a degree of risk, some are riskier than others. Emmanuel learnt that there are also high-risk high-return investments.

Abigail used the example of a privately owned company that decides to list on the stock exchange and go public. This generates great anticipation that the shares will grow quickly so investors buy up the shares, and this increases demand. At this point, two things could happen: either the company does well and there are big returns, or the company does very badly leading to low returns.

In the latter scenario, if the share price drops below their purchase price, an investor could lose all their money. Abigail explained that if Emmanuel decided to start an investment portfolio, the bank would make the investments on his behalf and charge him fees for doing this. She also discussed retirement policies, disability, and health insurance. Emmanuel was interested in all of these but was not sure whether he could afford them. Abigail noted

Emmanuel's concerns and showed him how much it would cost. The monthly premiums were far less than he'd expected, and they were manageable, so he signed up for all three. He also signed up for the ISA and invested four thousand, six hundred and thirty pounds of his savings in it. With the remaining five hundred pounds he invested in medium risk shares as he was willing to take some risk. Abigail made quite sure that he understood that he could end up losing all his money if he invested in these shares, as the returns were not guaranteed. Emmanuel was aware of the risk and confirmed that he still wanted to go ahead.

Abigail took him through all the terms and conditions and made sure that he understood everything he was about to sign, including the charges. He was happy with everything and signed all the documents including the authority to debit his account for the ISA, medium-risk shares, retirement, disability, and health insurance policy. Before leaving the meeting, Abigail showed him how to download an app to monitor his investments.

On his way home he had a million thoughts flying through his head. He couldn't wait to see how quickly his money was going to grow.

Every day Emmanuel checked the app and became increasingly frustrated as he couldn't see any growth. After a week, he called Abigail to find out what was happening, and she reminded him that he needed to take a medium- to long-term view when investing in shares. Looking at the share price everyday expecting a high return would result in disappointment. At the same time, a return wasn't guaranteed! She stressed this point during the call just to make sure that Emmanuel was aware of the risks. He felt a little uneasy but decided that he would give it time. A few months passed before Emmanuel noticed at last that his share portfolio had begun to grow.

With regards to his business, the team he had hired was performing well. However, he noticed that some of his loyal customers only requested garden services every three to four months, and this came with certain challenges. There were some months where he could not find space to fit them in as he was fully booked, and when he did have space, they did not need him. To overcome this challenge, Emmanuel decided to offer his customers a maintenance contract that ran for six or twelve months. The contracts would work out far cheaper than the daily rate. He gambled on the fact that having to do a garden every month would have three benefits: he would have consistent income, monthly scheduling for his team would be easier, and lastly, although the customer paid less for the service, the work would be easier and quicker to do as his team was doing the garden more regularly. His loyal customers loved the idea and signed up for the maintenance contracts. The split between contracts and one-off customers was about sixty/forty, and over a few months he found that if his team did an excellent job with the one-off customers, they soon moved to a maintenance contract.

Emmanuel's business growth allowed him to save more than what he had anticipated, and after a year and a half had passed, he was thrilled to see that all his investments, including the ISA, were now worth twenty-seven thousand, three hundred and fifty pounds. He was finally ready to purchase his first property! He found a great one-bedroomed flat that cost one hundred and thirteen thousand pounds. His offer was accepted, and he had enough to pay a 20% deposit for the flat. The bank approved his mortgage and gave him a more favourable interest rate due to the size of his deposit. Emmanuel felt justified in taking on this debt as he considered the property to be an investment: it was likely to be worth more in a few years' time, besides he could not live in his dad's house indefinitely. Life was certainly going well for Emmanuel, and he loved his new home.

He continued to save and invest in the stock market but there were also tough times. He experienced the reality that medium-risk does not always mean medium-return, such as the time he lost a lot of money when the shares took a tumble during a global financial crisis. He also learnt a hard lesson about accepting investment advice. **A friend of his convinced him to invest one thousand pounds in shares that were going to make him a fortune, yet instead of growing they lost all their value overnight and he lost everything. The friend that gave him the advice was no expert and would not cover his loss.** Emmanuel kicked himself for listening to him, and from that time on, vowed to only take advice from a professional.

Emmanuel was a very generous man and regularly donated money to the church he attended as well as to those in need. His business kept growing and now he had over one thousand homes on his books and thirty-two people working for him. He wanted to expand but had not saved enough to cover the cost of more equipment, storage space and resources; as a result, he was turning business away to his competitors. The bank had contacted him on a few occasions, as they had some lending offers which they believed his business would benefit from. He was tempted, but in the end, he always declined as he continued to hold the belief that debt would eat away at his profits.

One evening he met with Gabriel, a good friend of his who was also running his own company. Over a game of pool, the conversation moved onto their businesses. Emmanuel said his company was doing brilliantly and he could easily expand but was a little low on cash for all the things he wanted to do.

"Why don't you get finance for the expansion?"

"I have thought of this many times, but I don't want to pay the bank interest and fees for a loan, as it will only eat away at my business profits," Emmanuel replied.

"Do you really believe that?"

"Yes, and another reason I don't want to take a loan is because of what happened to my brother. As you know, his business failed and because my dad signed surety, he lost everything as well." Emmanuel sighed as he said this.

Gabriel listened attentively then asked a straightforward question. "Do you think your business will fail like your brother's did?"

"No, definitely not, mine is financially sound and is going along nicely."

"Then why are you treating your business as if it was your brother's business?"

Emmanuel could not answer that. He just reiterated that he did not want a loan because he didn't want his business to have debt.

Gabriel persisted: "Look, taking a loan could help you finance your expansion. In addition, all the extra expenses are tax deductible, and you will benefit from that when you do your tax returns. When I used my opportunity to get finance, my business grew so much that I was able to pay off the debt much quicker than I had expected. The profits from my expansion have been far greater than the costs associated with the loan I had taken."

"It's something to think about," Emmanuel said, and left it at that. Gabriel's words both excited and frightened him and he did not sleep well that night. The truth was that he had become so anti-debt that he had closed himself off to any opportunities that might exist through taking a loan.

In the morning he checked all his finances, factored in the cost of the debt to his business, as well as the returns he would make through the expansion. He realised that Gabriel was right, the loan made financial sense and it was a risk he was willing to take.

Emmanuel called his bank and made an appointment to see them. After he'd completed an application for a short-term loan, the bank's system offered him a loan that was slightly larger than what he needed. He declined the larger amount as he knew that it could only lead to him getting into more debt. **His new belief was that any loan he took had to be used for generating profit, or it would simply become a costly expense.** Emmanuel used the money for the expansion, and it was a remarkable success.

Gabriel was right: he made much more money than the costs associated with the loan, and as a result he managed to pay it off much sooner than he had projected.

His friends could see that he was doing incredibly well, yet one thing puzzled them: why was he still driving an old car? It made no sense. When they challenged him on this, he always explained that his car was fully paid off, and he could see no financial reason to get a new one and anyway, the money could be better spent elsewhere. The irony was that when it came to his business, all his equipment was new, vehicles included. Emmanuel bought brand-new equipment every time because of all the associated tax benefits, as well as the warranties and maintenance contracts a new purchase offered.

By the time Emmanuel retired, he was a very wealthy man and had become a philanthropist. He created a trust fund to support people from underprivileged backgrounds, so that they could study without the burden of having to pay back debt. In his old age Emmanuel enjoyed all the fruits of his labour and got to travel to many parts of the world. Life was wonderful.

14. Olivia's Journey

Olivia was crushed beneath the weight of her guilt. Why hadn't she taken time to consider the consequences of her fury? What was to become of Jason? Her reaction surprised her, for as vicious as her wrath had been, her feelings of guilt and sadness were even more intense. She was still in tears when her husband arrived home from work. As soon as Mark saw her face, he wanted to know what was wrong.

"Jason has been expelled and now his life is ruined because of me!"

Mark replied, "Nonsense Olivia. He got himself expelled and his life is not ruined. This is not your fault as it is a consequence of his aggressive behaviour."

"You're wrong. It was all because of me! If I had just been calm none of this would have happened!" she cried remorsefully.

"You did nothing wrong, Olivia." Mark tried to calm her, but nothing was working. "Let me make you a cappuccino," he said, instinctively knowing that the action of sipping a hot drink would help to calm her down. Olivia nodded and continued to pour out her heart.

As she sipped her cappuccino, she thought of a thousand things she could have done differently. Who was this Jason really, and why had he sworn at her? What was his home life like, could she have helped him? What were the other students going to think of her when they heard that she'd got him expelled? Was this what she really wanted? Olivia shared many of her thoughts with Mark as they sat at the kitchen table. He was a great listener and because of their conversation she decided that she would discuss her concerns with Mrs Brown, the principal of the school.

The next morning Olivia was late for the staff meeting. She apologised to her colleagues and blamed the traffic, but the truth was that she had not slept well because of a combination of guilt about Jason and her stress at what she would say to Mrs Brown. In the meeting she did her best to hide her distress but whenever she looked up, she saw the concerned faces of her colleagues. Mrs Brown asked her to stay behind when the rest of the staff went to their classes.

"How are you feeling, Olivia?" Mrs Brown asked sympathetically.

Olivia's tears spilled over again as she replied, "To tell you the truth I feel gutted, I never wanted this to happen."

Mrs Brown spoke softly, trying to comfort her younger colleague. "I understand, it is never easy dealing with a difficult student, of course, but I am glad we were able to do the right thing. The school is much safer now."

Olivia asked tremulously, "Have we done the right thing? This boy has his whole life ahead of him."

The principal's response led to a lengthy conversation, and Olivia came to understand that the decision to expel Jason was not a result of this one incident alone, but rather due to a history of incidents. Teachers and pupils alike needed to be in a safe environment.

After the meeting, Olivia called Mark to tell him what had happened, and her tears flowed as relief overwhelmed her. Mark was pleased to hear that she was feeling better and reminded her that they had an appointment later that day to see a house they both liked.

That evening they viewed a large, detached house in a good area and were both impressed with its spaciousness. The fireplace melted Olivia's heart, and she imagined cosy winter evenings in front of the fire, curled up on the couch with Mark. It was so romantic!

Mark, on the other hand, saw that the property needed a lot of work. The garden was overgrown and was full of weeds, the walls needed a new coat of paint, and the kitchen counters were rotten and had to be replaced. He made a few calculations in his head and the figure made him wince, but the house did have potential.

"I want it!" Olivia whispered.

Mark replied, "So do I."

In the car on the way home they discussed all the things they loved about the house and the things that needed to be changed. They both agreed that the kitchen counters were non-negotiable and the rest they could live with for now. A few days later, the negotiations for the house were finalised. They applied for a mortgage with their local bank, and it was approved—right at the maximum limit that the bank would grant them. One of the conditions of the mortgage was that they would take life policies on each other's lives, to ensure that the proceeds from the policy would repay the mortgage in the unlikely event of one or both dying prematurely. The bank would take cession of these policies to ensure that it had first rights to the policy should anything happen to the Wards. The bank also required a deposit of fifty-five thousand pounds. This completely emptied their savings account, leaving only a little for the birth of their baby who was due in two months' time. The renovations that were needed in the house would have to wait, at least until March the following year when Mark got his bonus. Despite it all, Olivia and Mark were both over the moon to have their own property.

The day finally arrived for them to move into their new house, and it was chaotic, there were boxes everywhere. Fortunately, Olivia's folks were there to help. The timing of the move couldn't have been more perfect as the following week Olivia went into labour. Mark suspected that the stress of the move may have had something to do with it. A few hours later Olivia gave birth to a healthy baby boy. They instantly fell in love with him and named him Leonard after Olivia's dad.

The first three months after his birth were challenging: they had not realised just how much work a baby would bring. There were so many broken nights because of Leonard's crying, and they were unable to unpack all the boxes from the move. Money became very tight, and Mark decided to use his overdraft to meet some of their monthly expenses.

A few years earlier when he'd opened his account, the bank had offered him an overdraft of one thousand pounds which, they said, would help in those unplanned-for moments. They explained that an overdraft meant if he had used all his money and had a zero balance in his bank account, he could still use his card to purchase items. However, he would no longer be using his own money (as the balance was zero), but instead he'd be using the bank's money, and every month they'd charge him thirty seven percent interest per annum on whatever amount he'd used. They did stress that the overdraft was for short-term needs only. At the time of opening the account, he'd felt that it was an easy decision, because it would give him a buffer if there ever was an emergency. Surely now was that time.

Mark quickly used up the entire overdraft and started paying over thirty pounds in interest every month as he was not able to pay off the overdraft straight away. He was horrified at the costs and felt that he had to do something about this. He remembered seeing an advert that his bank offered personal loans with an interest rate of five percent which was so much lower than the thirty seven percent he was currently paying. He applied for the loan, only for it to be declined as his credit record had dropped due to buying the house and using his whole overdraft. He was bitterly disappointed with the decision and embarrassed at the same time.

The costs of running the home kept on increasing and, at the same time, Mark began to struggle with his

mental health because he couldn't tell Olivia how much debt he was accumulating.

After a few months of being in the new house, Olivia was ready to purchase a new car. The one she had was old and she feared for their child's safety as there were no airbags.

When Mark heard about Olivia's plan, he said: "I don't think this is a great idea Olivia, as our expenses have gone up since we moved to this house."

Olivia did not understand why he was being so negative. "I make more than enough money to pay for a new car, and I am managing my expenses just fine."

Mark was not honest about the financial struggles he was going through and simply replied, "I still don't think you should buy a new car."

"Well," she said briskly, "We could swap cars if you like. Your car's safety features would be perfect for Leonard."

"No," he said. "That's not going to happen. I often attend client meetings and I need to make a good impression."

"Hmph." Olivia continued, "how about you giving up golf? The savings from doing this would more than cover the increased expenses about which you are so worried."

They were close to getting into an argument when Mark backed off. "I suppose I could play less often..." he said reluctantly. "What kind of car did you have in mind?"

Olivia was still feeling surprised at Mark's initial response to her getting a new car. He was not normally so snappy.

"Mark, is there something wrong?"

"No, nothing, my love," he said quickly, yet Olivia could tell that he was not being honest.

After a little bit of prodding, Mark said he'd had a dreadful day at the office and apologised for taking it out on her. That same week, Olivia visited a few car dealers in the area and soon found the car she wanted. The dealership 'sweetened' the deal by offering her a great trade-in for her old car, and when she applied for vehicle finance, her excellent credit record meant that the loan was approved straight away. The cost was only an extra one hundred pounds a month for the next sixty months—although her car insurance did go up by an extra forty pounds a month.

Mark was coping with his personal debt but had got into the bad habit of paying off debt and then building it up again. This cycle kept him in debt and made things more financially pressurised. Then one fateful Saturday, he heard terrible news. The Bank of England had raised the interest rate as a strategy to help lower inflation. Shortly afterwards his bank notified him that they were raising the interest rates. As a result, the monthly repayments on their mortgage as well as his other debts were about to increase substantially.

The stress was too much for Mark and he turned to alcohol to calm himself down. However, this did not solve his financial problems, it just numbed his feelings towards them. Olivia saw the change in his behaviour, but he refused to be honest about what was really going on. There were many late nights where Mark came home drunk. Olivia tried her best to encourage him to stop, but he would not listen. The financial pressure from rising interest rates had started to get to Olivia as well. She too was finding it difficult to cope with less money and could not understand how Mark could waste so much cash on alcohol as well as paying for his weekly games of golf. This was so selfish! Why didn't he put his family first?

One night she confronted him as he arrived home. "Mark, please stop drinking, we really need the extra cash."

This set Mark off and he roared at Olivia, "You put us in this position, you wanted the new car, I told you not to get it!"

His extremely hurtful words made her scream back: "You're an alcoholic, and your drinking has put us in this position! As for your golf, why don't you quit?"

As Lenny began to wail, Olivia's jibes threw Mark over the edge.

"How dare you? I am the main breadwinner! Golf is the only thing I spend money on for myself, the rest goes to you. You got us into this mess and now you are expecting *me* to get us out of it?"

Olivia completely lost her temper. "You, the main breadwinner? You do nothing. I have a full-time job and then when I get home, I clean and cook for you, so what the hell do you do? How much would you pay for someone to cook and clean for you? You pay me nothing. I am contributing towards the mortgage. I also look after baby Lenny, and you do nothing to help. You think the world revolves around you."

The argument came to a terrible end when Olivia found herself screaming angrily: "I want a divorce!"

Mark spat out: "And so do I!" He stormed out of the house, slamming the door behind him.

She picked up their 'circle of friends' wedding gift that had been given to them by a close friend and threw it against the wall. The heavy ornament smashed into little pieces, and she couldn't help thinking that the fragments on the carpet were symbolic of her marriage. It too had fallen apart.

Over the weeks that followed, the fighting got more intense, and Mark often disappeared for hours on end. On one of these occasions Olivia waited up for him. When he arrived home at last, she cornered him in the kitchen.

"Where were you?" she said accusingly.

"It has nothing to do with you," he snapped as he opened the fridge and grabbed a can of beer.

She composed herself as she did not want to wake Leonard up. "I have been looking after Lenny all on my own, where were you?"

Mark retorted: "All you do is complain. I am the one carrying this family, not you."

Olivia could not believe what he was saying. His breath stank of alcohol, and she'd had enough of listening to his abuse. She opened her mouth to give him an earful but, before she could speak, he'd disappeared out the house and slammed the front door behind him.

Sobbing, she wrote a letter, shoved it into an envelope and left it on the kitchen table.

He arrived back a few hours later and stumbled through to the kitchen. The envelope had been placed exactly where Mark poured his drinks, and even in his drunken state he could not miss it. Opening the letter he read, "*I want a divorce.*" This just made him angry, and he shouted, "I also want a divorce!"

Olivia was sleeping inside her locked room with Lenny and the scream woke them both up. Clearly, he had read her letter. The next day the house was silent. Mark called in sick as he had a massive headache and apart from that he was emotionally drained. Olivia's letter was so much more serious now that he had sobered up. He tried to speak to Olivia, but she refused to talk to him. He sent texts, and tried calling her, yet no answer was forthcoming except for one text: "I want a divorce."

As the days passed, he became desperate. In the cold light of day, he did not want to lose his marriage. In desperation, he called a confidential helpline and spoke with a lady named Elizabeth. The call was a long one and Mark explained everything that was going on in his marriage, and how fearful he was of losing his wife and child. Elizabeth asked a few questions and gave him some practical steps to deal with the stress. However, she pointed out that it would be a good idea for Mark and his wife to go to family counselling.

After the call Mark felt a bit better and wrote Olivia a letter.

Dear Olivia, I realise that the last few weeks have not been easy. I have been so selfish in not being there for you and I wish I could go back and do things differently. I love you and Lenny so much and really want our relationship to work. I know I have not been easy to get on with. I have spoken with someone on a helpline, and they suggested we go for family counselling. Please, would you consider going with me?

Olivia read the letter through her tears. She was so tired of Mark shouting at her and treating her like she was worthless. Yet, despite her emotion, there was also an element of scepticism in her mind as she read the letter. He hadn't even said sorry, or was the 'I have been so selfish' an actual apology? She doubted it. Her anger burned as she pondered whether, with all those late nights, he'd been unfaithful to her. How *could* he have an affair when she was the mother of their child? Counselling might help to get to the bottom of it.

15. The Counsellor

Mark and Olivia arrived at the marriage counsellor's office and took their seats in the waiting room alongside an elderly couple. The cheerful pop song playing over the speakers was in harsh contrast to the cold emotions flowing in the room, and Olivia felt that the music was in poor taste. She could not bring herself to look at Mark as he had hurt her so badly. After some minutes a tall, willowy woman who could have been a model hurried into the waiting room and invited them to join her in her office. She looked far too young to be a counsellor, Mark thought.

Inside the large office, on the other side of the desk, there were three easy chairs arranged around a small coffee table which held a tray with two glasses and a jug of iced water. Mark and Olivia each took a seat and the counsellor settled herself in the remaining chair.

She said calmly, "My name is Akanya, and I am so pleased that you have come to see me today."

As she began to list her qualifications and counselling experience, Mark relaxed. This was obviously not the first time she had followed this process; many others must have questioned her credentials because of her young looks.

"Now tell me a little about yourselves and what has brought you to this point," Akanya said.

Olivia described the pressures she was facing, and her financial worries. She complained that lately Mark had been unsupportive and often disappeared all night, which made her feel like she was a single parent. As soon as she uttered these words, he tried to interrupt but the counsellor stopped him firmly and said he would get his turn. Olivia spilt her heart out and shared everything—it was like she had opened a tap and could not close it. Mark looked on uncomfortably as his wife wept. Finally, she fell silent, and Akanya thanked her for being so open and honest.

Then she turned to Mark. "What has brought you to this point?"

He told her about the huge financial burden he was carrying for the whole family, how his wife had got them into debt, and how he was the one having to get them out of the mess. When asked to elaborate, he spoke about Olivia buying the new car.

"How does that make you feel?" Akanya asked.

"It makes me feel terrible. I have sleepless nights and every time I ask her to reign in her spending, she spends more. I blame her for this mess."

Olivia could not hold back. "Hang on, *you* put us in this mess. You're an alcoholic and you spend so much money on golf. You are away from Leonard and me all the time, and on top of that, you are having an affair!"

Akanya waited.

Mark was bewildered. He looked straight at Olivia and said firmly, "I am not having an affair."

She snapped back, "Then where are you until the early hours of the morning?"

Mark would not answer.

Akanya asked Olivia how she felt about Mark coming home so late.

Olivia struggled to compose herself. Her emotions were now laid bare, and she could hardly speak. In between sobs all she could say was, "I do not know who he is anymore. How can he abandon me and our baby at the time I need him most?" She felt her anger rise again. "He is just a self-absorbed narcissist."

Akanya turned to Mark and asked quietly: "How do you feel about what Olivia is saying?"

He steadied his harsh breathing and responded, "I am really upset at being falsely accused, I am not having an affair and have never been unfaithful to her!"

A few minutes passed in silence and Mark felt incredibly uncomfortable.

Then Akanya asked Mark again: "How are you feeling?"

Something snapped inside at being asked the same question again. "You want me to tell you how I am feeling? I am feeling overwhelmed, and Olivia does nothing to help me!"

Akanya prodded, "What are you feeling overwhelmed about?"

He had been keeping a secret for the past few months, but the intensity of this conversation was too much for him, he had to get it off his chest. "I have

been gambling and have got into so much debt that I...." At that point he stopped. He had shared too much.

"How much debt?" Olivia asked icily.

He lied about the amount, but even the lie was more money than Olivia made in a year.

"How could you *do* this to us?" she shouted, completely disregarding the receptionist and the others in the waiting room.

Mark wept as he spluttered, "I thought I could win."

For the rest of the session, Akanya encouraged them to talk through what had been shared. This was the most talking they had done in many months. At the end of the session, they scheduled another appointment for the following week.

Strangely enough, whenever Olivia and Mark spoke to each other in the days that followed, there was a lot less sting in their words and they spent more time together with baby Lenny.

The counselling sessions continued for the next few months, and on some occasions they each saw Akanya on their own. **Through the therapy Olivia and Mark realised that they still loved each other, and they came to understand that their problem was not with their relationship, but rather with the financial difficulties they were going through.** They also learnt that they were not the only ones who fought about money. There were in fact many couples who got divorced because of financial problems.

At their last therapy session, Akanya congratulated them for making so much progress and she highly recommended that they see a financial consultant. They both thanked Akanya as she had done wonders for their marriage.

16. The Investigation

They both liked the counsellor's idea of getting professional help with their finances as it was still a thorn in their flesh. Mark contacted his bank to see if they could recommend someone, and they gave him contact details for a trusted financial consultant who had specialist knowledge of helping people with financial difficulties. The appointment was set for Tuesday the following week and they were told to bring an extensive list of documents with them. Olivia made three phone calls and her documents were ready for the appointment, but Mark struggled to find and organise his papers. She offered to help but he insisted that he was okay and would have everything ready in time.

When Tuesday arrived, they drove to the financial consultant's offices. Surprisingly, the address was in a rundown part of town where there was graffiti on the walls and the roads seemed eerily empty. Feeling uneasy, Olivia asked Mark to check the address. Surely this was not where they were meant to be going, she said worriedly, yet Mark insisted that it was. She was nervous and wanted to head back home, but he convinced her that they both needed the advice. When they did find the building, it was scruffy. This resulted in a further struggle to decide whether to keep the appointment or not. Standing at the door of the building they were confronted by a keypad of tiny buttons and illegible names. It was a dull and gloomy day and Olivia struggled to read the names of the tenants. Finally, she pressed the second button in the hope that it was for the financial consultant. As soon as she did so, a friendly voice announced over the speaker, "Taylor Financial Consultancy. How can I help you?"

"We are here to see Derek," replied Olivia with relief.

"And you are?"

"Olivia and Mark Ward."

"We are expecting you," the pleasant female voice replied. "Please take the stairs to the second floor as the elevator is under repair."

Olivia felt that this was certainly the most unprofessional organisation she had ever dealt with. The stairway leading up to the second floor smelt musty and there were cobwebs everywhere. She decided at once that this would be their first and last appointment with this consultant, and that 7they would lodge a complaint with the bank about their experience.

They eventually made it to the second floor where pots of paint and scaffolding planks lined the hall, and followed the passage to the office where, to their astonishment, they saw a new red-carpet runner laid on the floor outside the door. This carpet really did not fit in with the surrounding building work! Entering the offices, both Olivia and Mark were pleasantly surprised by the contrast between what they'd just experienced outside and the pristine carpet and couches. The reception desk was solid oak with a marble counter and was lit by carefully positioned light fittings.

The friendly receptionist stood up to greet them. "Hello. My name is Cindy. I do apologise for any inconvenience caused by the renovations."

Mark replied politely, "It's no problem at all."

"Derek will be with you shortly," the woman said and invited them to sit in the waiting area.

After a minute or two, a tall, well-dressed man appeared. Derek introduced himself and ushered the couple into his spacious office.

"Please take a seat," Derek said, indicating two smart grey couches flanking an oak coffee table. "Good afternoon to you both. I do hope the trip getting here was not too unpleasant?"

Mark replied, "Well we did wonder whether we had the right building…"

Derek chuckled. "Absolutely. I know of others that have turned around and cancelled their appointments. We are part of an urban renewal project which will take about two years to complete. Nevertheless, I am really pleased that you persevered. Now, do you have all the documents I asked for?"

"Yes, it was a long list," replied Olivia.

"My apologies for the lengthy list, but it is the only way I can see exactly what is going on with your finances. Before we go through the documents, why don't you tell me what led to you coming to see me?"

Olivia spoke about the house, baby, car, and the huge debt, and Mark threw in the odd sentence or two.

"To sum it up," she concluded, "our finances are in a mess, and we don't know how to fix them."

"Olivia, how did your finances get to this point?" Derek asked.

She thought about it and suggested tentatively, "We made some wrong decisions."

Derek nodded his head and then said, "What about you, Mark? What do you think?"

"I really don't know. It is a question I have asked myself so many times and I just don't know the answer."

"What have you both tried to do to improve your position so far?"

Mark looked at the ground sheepishly and then answered, "I initially tried to get a higher paying job, but I was unsuccessful. And then, when I got desperate, I tried gambling in the hope of getting lucky but that only made things worse."

Derek was surprised at Mark's answer. Usually, his clients were not so honest!

Mark continued, "But I stopped gambling four months ago and I have joined a gambling support group."

Derek thanked Mark for his candour and affirmed that gambling was the quickest way to not only destroy finances but also relationships; it was a dangerous thing to do, especially for those in debt.

"What about you, Olivia, what have you done to get out of debt?"

"I guess I've stayed at home more to ensure that I spend less, and I've asked my mum to help care for Leonard while I'm teaching."

Derek asked, "Is Leonard your son?"

"Yes," Olivia responded proudly. "Our baby boy. He's just over a year now."

Derek took a few notes and then said, "Before we go further, how serious are both of you about becoming financially stable?"

Mark replied, "Very serious. We really want to get our finances in order."

"That is good to hear. I must warn you that the road ahead is not going to be an easy one, and some of the things I will ask you to do are incredibly tough, but if you are serious, it is a road worth taking," the financial consultant said soberly.

Mark mumbled that it sounded over-dramatic, but he would soon learn how true those words were.

"This appointment serves as a fact-finding exercise. You'll both need to be completely honest if I'm to help you," Derek said, laying the foundation for all future appointments.

Mark and Olivia assured him that they would be honest because they desperately needed his help with their finances.

"Let's start with your bank statements," Derek said to Mark. He laid three months' worth of statements on the table. Derek looked through them as he asked questions, and circled items in an assortment of colours according to Mark's answers. Many of the questions made Mark squirm because the transactions in his bank statements revealed so much about his spending habits.

"What about your loan statements?"

"Here they are," Mark said as he produced three more statements.

Once again Derek asked questions and circled items. Then he asked, "Do you have any credit card statements?"

Mark nodded his head sheepishly and gave him another two sets of statements. When Olivia saw this, she started to panic—it was the first time she had seen the extent of Mark's debt and she had many questions she wanted to ask him. She wondered whether she had made the right choice in staying with him.

Derek asked, "Are there any more accounts?"

"Yes, one more," Mark said very quietly as he handed over another document.

Olivia now understood why they'd been given a two-hour appointment. But why had it taken so long for her husband to be honest about his debt?

"Do you have copies of all the legal agreements?" Derek asked.

"Yes," Mark sighed and handed these over.

"How did you arrange the loans? And what were you advised when you applied for them?" Derick scribbled something on one of the documents as Mark answered the questions he had asked. "Are you aware of any other accounts?"

Mark replied "No, this is it."

Derek took Olivia through the same process. She had a bank account, store account and vehicle loan. There was also a joint mortgage account, but he'd already covered this with Mark.

Their two hours were soon up. Derek ended the appointment with two clear instructions: Firstly, they were not to discuss each other's finances as it would only lead to arguments and secondly, they needed to record all their cash purchases.

17. The Debt

Two weeks later they were back in Derek's office.

"Good to see you both," he said as he started the meeting. "How has your week been?"

Olivia replied that they had done their homework and had also argued about Mark's debt.

At this, Mark snapped back, "And your debt too."

Derek did not want the two of them to get into an argument and quickly interrupted. "Thank you for doing your homework. When I spoke with you last week, I made a few circles on your bank statement using assorted colours. I am sure you wondered what they were about. The brown circles are all your debt repayments: these include your mortgage, vehicle, loans, credit cards and store cards. The yellow circles are your monthly repayments for things like rates, insurance, water, and lights. The blue circles are your expenses relating to food and drink. The red circles are payments for entertainment, such as golf, the odd takeaway, parking tickets and the like. The purple circles indicate those unaccounted-for amounts where you drew cash from the bank. The black circles are for your savings. What I am going to do is go through each of the circles with you and we can then agree on the way forward. Would that be okay with you?"

Both Mark and Olivia nodded.

"Let's start with your homework, the purple circles. Do you have any information on this week's cash withdrawals?"

"Yes, I drew ten pounds in cash to contribute towards a birthday present for a colleague," said Olivia.

"I drew forty pounds to pay a friend some money I owed him," said Mark. As soon as he said this, he regretted it. He hadn't told Olivia or Derek about the money he had borrowed from his friend.

"Do you owe money to anyone else, Mark?" Derek asked quietly.

"No, I just owe this same friend another three hundred and sixty pounds."

Olivia was mortified. If it were not for how far they had come recently, she would not have had the strength to stay with Mark. He had really messed up.

"All right, thanks for the honesty. Did either of you draw cash for anything else?"

"I also took out twenty pounds to buy some fruit from the grocer," Olivia responded. "I don't think there were any other withdrawals last week."

Derek responded, "The seventy pounds you drew last week was a lot less than the two hundred and twenty pounds you drew out during the previous week. What changed?"

Mark sat silently for a minute or two and then couldn't bear it anymore. "I didn't play golf this week."

Derek thanked them. "The key to the purple circles is that we always need to know what we are spending and why we are spending it," he said. "We will now discuss your loans, indicated by the brown circles."

Mark was uneasy as he knew most of the debt was his.

"Collectively you have taken out thirty-five thousand pounds' worth of loans. Your store card, overdraft and credit card are all at their maximum limit and three months ago you took out another loan. We will discuss that shortly. There is also a joint mortgage that is two months in arrears."

Olivia muttered to herself, "How is that even possible?" She could not believe how much debt Mark had accumulated; it was far worse than he had admitted at the councillor's office.

Derek continued, "Once you have paid off the thirty-five thousand pounds, how much do you think you would have paid in total?"

"Forty-two thousand pounds?" Mark guessed.

Derek replied, "No. You would in effect pay fifty-eight thousand, five hundred and fifty-two pounds—and a few pence. That is twenty-three thousand, five hundred and twenty-two pounds more than what you borrowed."

"That's madness." Mark said in disbelief.

Derek quickly responded, "**Most of what you will pay in the initial months is just interest, and in effect you are being charged interest on the interest you owe for these loans. This is called the compounding effect.**

With high interest rates you are always going to pay a lot more than you borrowed."

Mark felt like he had been robbed. "How could they do this?"

"Quite easily. The banks take a risk when they lend people money, and that risk is factored in by charging higher interest rates."

Derek looked in Mark's direction as he continued. "Regarding the most recent loan you took out: I'd like you to go through the process you followed to get the loan."

Mark explained how he searched for the loan online and then described the process he'd followed to complete the loan. He had been surprised when he was approved but was equally grateful as he was short on money.

Derek nodded, "This confirms my suspicions. This loan may fall into the category of reckless lending. The organisation you loaned from clearly should not have given you any money because at that stage you were already struggling to pay off your existing loans. There are some mitigating circumstances for the loan company: the information you provided them was inaccurate as you overstated your income and understated your expenses. However, they should have been able to see this through their credit checks. We can make a complaint against the organisation and see how they respond."

Derek looked across at Olivia. "You only have two loans: your store card which is almost at its limit, and your vehicle finance which has thirty-seven months' worth of instalments to go, although the interest rate seems quite high. We may be able to do something about that."

Olivia relaxed a little, only to tense up as Derek brought up her spending on the store card.

"On the grocery store card two weeks ago, you spent one hundred and eleven pounds, twenty-three pence. By the time you've paid it off, that shopping will cost you one hundred and sixty-three pounds, fifty-two pence."

Olivia thought: *Why is this guy being so specific? It's annoying.*

Derek asked her, "If you'd known it was going to cost you an extra fifty-two pounds to use the store card, would you have purchased these groceries with the card?"

Olivia responded, "Absolutely not."

Derek said, **"It important to realize the cost of money. Every time you use your credit or store cards, or take a loan, there is always a cost involved.** No matter how tempting it is to use these cards, you both need to understand that in effect you're paying far more than the price shown on the goods."

He gave them a moment to digest this, then continued: "You may be tempted to challenge me on this and remind me of the exclusive offers where there's no interest if you repay the full amount in a certain number of days. However, for most people it is impossible to pay the full amount within the stipulated time."

Derek then went through the yellow circles with them which indicated their electricity and insurance payments; he wanted to know how long they had been with these service providers. Both Olivia and Mark said that that they had been with them for several years. Derek made note of their comments and said it was likely that they could save some money on these bills as well. Moving on to the red circles, he explained that most of the entertainment expenses were for the golf games, satellite television, mobile phone contracts and coffee shops. He said that all these expenses would need to be reviewed soon. The blue circles showed that the monthly shopping bill was on average four hundred and twenty-three pounds but there was money to be saved here too. Derek mentioned that there were no black circles as he could not pick up any savings. Both Olivia and Mark agreed with him as they had given up trying to find spare cash to save.

"After going through all your finances, would you like to guess how much you are overspending in relation to how much you are earning each month?"

"Two hundred and thirty pounds?" Olivia guessed.

"I think two hundred and fifty," Mark added.

"Well actually, it's quite a bit more, I'm afraid. Currently, you are spending three hundred pounds and thirty-seven pence more than you are earning each month. In effect, you spend way more than you earn."

"Are you sure that's correct?" Olivia whispered, shocked at the amount.

Derek nodded his head and said, "Yes, I am afraid it is."

He waited for this to sink in before saying: "Knowing what I have just shared with you about your finances, what do you think needs to happen next?"

Olivia responded swiftly, "We must stop using the cards."

Derek said, "Correct, but what is the key thing we need to achieve to get you both out of the debt you are in?"

They looked blankly at him.

Derek paused then said softly, **"Our priority is to bring your monthly expenses below your income. This way you will be able to start paying off debt and at the same time you may be able to save some money."**

Derek said soberly: "The challenge is that if your monthly expenses are higher than your income, you will not be able to get out of debt and, what is worse, your debt will increase."

Mark felt that Derek's words made sense but couldn't see how he would ever get his income to be higher than his expenses, let alone save money. He looked at Derek and asked, "How will we ever earn more than our expenses? Must we get higher paying jobs? I tried that and it didn't happen!"

Derek nodded thoughtfully. "I hear your distress. It seems like an impossible task, but I can assure you that over the next few weeks, if you follow through on the agreed actions, it will happen. You won't need to earn more money once you spend less."

Mark still wasn't sure. "But how can we do that?"

Olivia snapped, "Give Derek a chance. I am sure he will tell us."

Derek nodded his head in agreement. "I'll speak about that next week. Your homework is to create a spreadsheet and record everything you spend during the week, not just the cash withdrawals but everything that passes through your accounts, as well as the reason you've spent the money."

Olivia and Mark were both grateful that Derek ended the session there as their brains were exhausted.

18. The Budget

The following week they returned to Derek's office with their homework. They had not fought with each other, which was a good start, possibly because they'd been kept busy with recording everything, they spent money on. They felt that exercise was worthwhile and eye-opening. Derek listened attentively and was pleased with their feedback.

"Congratulations on following through. I am glad to hear that you found the exercise beneficial. **Listing all your expenses is important as it is the first step in developing a plan. This plan, known as a budget, will help you avoid the trap of overspending.** A budget sets clear limits on everything you want to spend money on. These limits are like the speed limits on a road: if you keep to them, you will avoid getting a speeding fine, and in this case the fine would be more debt. Later I will explain how and where to set these limits, but for today I want us to focus on your monthly loan repayments. According to my calculations they are far too high."

"Fortunately, it is possible to reduce them by renegotiating with the loan companies for better rates or more favourable repayment plans." Derek pointed to a list. "Here's what we need to do. First, we'll speak to the micro lenders to see if we can negotiate better interest rates, and we'll raise a case of reckless lending for that online loan we discussed last week."

Turning to Olivia, he continued: "We should also call the finance company to see if they'll give you a better interest rate or extend the term of the loan on your vehicle and thus reduce your monthly repayments. We will then call the bank and ask them whether they would consider extending the existing twenty-year mortgage to a thirty-year mortgage, as this would reduce your monthly repayments and, at the same time, we can hopefully negotiate a better interest rate with them. Finally, we will call the companies who issued the credit cards and store cards to see if they are willing to reduce their rate of interest. Both Mark and Olivia were extremely impressed with Derek's proposal as it sounded positive!

Putting his phone on speaker, Derek rang the micro lender's call centre and selected the option to speak to a consultant regarding payment difficulties. The conversation went back and forth and eventually a manager at the call centre was able to approve a slight decrease in the interest rate. Derek then called another micro lender about the suspected case of reckless lending; however, this could not be resolved over the phone, and they were given a reference number with the promise that they would be notified once the investigation was complete. Derek also rang the bank's vehicle finance department, and this elicited a long wait. The outcome of this call was that the bank would not extend the vehicle repayment period, but they did agree to reduce the interest rate.

The next call was made to the bank to discuss the mortgage. Although it took a while to get through to the right person, it was worth the wait as the mortgage specialist agreed to restructure the loan to thirty years and reduce the interest rate slightly. This meant the account would no longer be in arrears. Mark and Olivia had some forms to fill in and the mortgage specialist emailed these through so that they could be completed and sent back straight away.

"Only two more phone calls," Derek said with satisfaction, "and that's to discuss the credit cards and store cards."

Mark breathed a sigh of relief. They were almost finished.

Both the credit card as well as store card companies agreed to better interest rates and repayment terms.

At this point **Derek handed them each a pair of scissors and asked them to cut up the credit and store cards. This scared Mark as the cards had been his safety blanket for a long time. What would he use now if he got into trouble?** Derek, noticing the fear in his eyes, assured him that it was the right thing to do. Mark and Olivia reluctantly went ahead and cut their cards into little pieces.

During the calls Derek had made notes of the savings they were making. Afterwards he said: "How much do you think you reduced your monthly repayments today?"

Mark replied, "Maybe two hundred pounds?"

Olivia said, "I think about two hundred and twenty pounds."

Derek smiled as he responded gleefully, "Three hundred and forty pounds!"

Mark and Olivia were astonished.

Derek continued, "That's the benefit of being transparent with your creditors—that is, those people to whom you owe money. They don't want to see you fail because they know that if you do, it is highly unlikely that they will get all their money back. I am certainly pleased with the result of the calls, and I can see that you are as well."

Both nodded their heads and smiled tiredly.

"That's it for today," Derek concluded. "The only thing left is your homework. I'd like you to continue with the spreadsheet and see if you can spend less than last week."

They agreed to do this and got up to leave. It had been an exhausting meeting, but they felt encouraged by the progress they'd made so far.

19. The Negotiation

The following week was tough and, as soon as they arrived at Derek's office, Olivia aired her frustrations.

"This week I went to buy some groceries and spent a couple of minutes searching for my card—only to realise that you'd made me cut it up last week. It was embarrassing! Derek, I am not sure that was the right thing to do. There is still credit available on that card."

Mark nodded his head in agreement. Derek listened to her complaint and calmly reassured Olivia that as their goal was to get out of debt, it was right to cut up the cards. He reminded the couple that when they used the cards, the cost of whatever they were purchasing became much higher because of the interest payments. The process they were going through would help them reach their debt-free destination and naturally there would be some bumps on the way but, when they finally got there, they would be overjoyed by the result.

He asked, "Do you want to continue with the process, or would you prefer to stop here? I'm afraid it's going to get even more difficult before it gets better."

Mark and Olivia agreed that they were willing to continue. Derek saw the look of apprehension on their faces and ploughed on.

"Good," he said. "Today's meeting will focus on reducing or eliminating unnecessary expenses. I note that you have Subscription based TV and that you have had it for two years. Have you renewed the contract recently?"

Mark thought about it for a while. "No, not that I know of."

Derek replied, "**Are you comfortable with cancelling the contract?**"

"**I'm not sure…**" Mark began. "**It would be embarrassing not to have subscription-based TV. What on earth would my friends think?**"

Derek said sternly: "If you are going to get out of debt, we need to reduce your expenses. You are paying thirty-five pounds a month for the subscription, and it is money you don't have."

Mark nodded slowly. "Yes, I see your point."

Derek got him to call the company from his office to cancel the contract.

"I also note that you have a subscription based streaming service. Are you willing to stop this as well?"

This time they agreed straight away. Olivia used her phone to go onto the website, log in and cancel the contract. Fortunately, they would still be able to watch the channel for another two weeks until their contract expired.

Next, he spoke about their mobile phone contracts. "Your monthly repayments seem high. What contracts do you have and when are these due for renewal?"

Mark said, "I think I renewed mine over a year ago."

"I haven't renewed mine," Olivia added. "I've been on the same package for the past few years."

Derek nodded. "Mark, I see that your phone bill changes every month—sometimes it's higher, sometimes lower. Why is that?"

Mark muttered, "Sometimes I have to purchase more data when I run out."

Derek responded firmly, "I don't think it's that. The fees are something to do with special SMSs and apps."

Mark cleared his throat and admitted that at times he entered competitions by sending an SMS that cost two pounds and he also used some betting apps on his phone to get up-to-date information on football games he was following. Olivia was visibly annoyed at this revelation but didn't say anything.

"Mark, are you willing to cancel all the app subscriptions and stop sending special SMS messages?" Derek enquired.

"Yes."

"You should also ask for clarification on the length of your phone contract and reduce it to a smaller package with lower fees as soon as possible."

"But I need extra data!" Mark said indignantly.

After a short but pointed discussion with Derek, Mark reluctantly agreed that he could use Wi-Fi at work and as most of the sites he visited were gambling sites, of which he agreed to stop visiting them, he didn't need that much mobile data anymore. A call to the mobile phone company showed that his contract would expire in three months' time and Mark asked them to put a restriction on his contract so that he would not incur any additional charges, which was something Derick had asked him to do. He was surprised to hear that they could do this! In future, Mark would only be charged for his contract; they would disable his ability to send special SMSs and stop any other charges from going through his mobile phone account.

Derek got Mark to put a reminder in his diary to downgrade his contract in three months' time. Olivia went through the same process and her mobile phone company agreed to downgrade her contract to a one-gig-a-month package from the five gig she had. This would save her ten pounds a month and she also put a hold on her account so that she would not have any extra charges besides her contract fee.

Derek had not finished. **"You should negotiate a better rate for both your car and home insurance. Olivia, you've been claim-free for five years and have always been with the same company. Could you check online for a cheaper rate?"**

She did so and found a vehicle policy that was forty pounds less per month; encouraged, she called her own insurance company to tell them about her intention to cancel the policy and they agreed to match the offered rate. For home insurance Olivia and Mark negotiated a better premium with their existing insurer.

Derek said that it might be worth consolidating some of their micro loans into one loan from their bank. However, before they did that, he wanted to get news on the reckless lending claim.

The meeting had only been scheduled for an hour and the time had gone by quite quickly. In closing Derek did some calculations then summarised all they had achieved so far. "When I first met you, you were in the red by three hundred pounds and thirty-seven pence. You are now in the green by eighty-four pounds and sixty-three pence. We have made some progress, but we are not there yet, there is still more to do."

Olivia and Mark were astonished that they now had money left over and couldn't help but smile. Derek gave them some more homework to complete before the next meeting in a month's time. Mark could no longer play golf and their very first goal was to spend three hundred and sixty pounds or less on groceries per month. They would have to compare the prices of everything and avoid the expensive stores and products. They had to stop all luxuries, such as chocolates and snacks, as well as going out for coffee with friends which Olivia loved. Mark would also have the challenging task of negotiating a payment plan with his friend to whom he still owed three hundred and sixty pounds. It felt like a shopping list and was quite overwhelming, but Derek assured them that this was all necessary. He promised to send them an email to remind them of what they needed to do.

20. The Discomfort

Mark went over his instructions repeatedly but there was no getting around it; negotiating payment terms with Philip would be highly embarrassing. While searching for a way to get around this problem, he decided to chat to his mother; this naturally led to her asking what was going on. Mark chose to be honest with her. However, the more he spoke, the more the blood drained from his mum's face; her concern for her son was obvious.

Mark assured her that he was turning his life around: they were seeing a financial consultant, and he had also begun attending support groups for gamblers and alcoholics anonymous.

His mother insisted on giving him the three hundred and sixty pounds he owed. "This is a gift from me," she said. "You do not need to pay this back."

"Thanks mum, it's nice of you to say that. But as soon as we are out of this predicament, I promise you I will pay back the money in full, plus the interest."

"No, you won't, this is my gift to you." His mum was adamant.

Later, Mark told Olivia what his mum had done. Olivia was so relieved that this debt had been sorted that she phoned to thank her mother-in-law straight away.

While it was initially difficult to adjust to not having subscription tv or the streaming service, they soon adapted to their new lifestyle. On the other hand, Olivia had been obliged to refuse numerous invitations to meet with her friends. She never told them the real reason—that there was no money—as this would have been too embarrassing, but she feared that at some point they would write her off as a friend if she didn't go out with them. Mark was fortunate enough to get a free game of golf at a work function, which relieved some of his stress. By week three Olivia and Mark were taking out their frustrations on each other and were having many arguments, which did not help matters, but despite this they both followed through on their homework. Week four was the longest week in both their lives.

Finally, the day of the appointment arrived, and they were both sitting in Derek's office. Olivia complained about the arguments they were having and how they were both struggling with all the restrictions.

Derek listened and nodded in agreement as Olivia spoke, and once she had finished offloading, he said: "I can hear that the month has not been easy, and it sounds like you both have been taking out your frustrations on each other."

Both Olivia and Mark simultaneously replied, "Yes" which made them smile.

Derek continued, "Breaking out of a comfort zone is incredibly difficult and what you have described is normal. But a month has gone past. Are you finding it easier or is it getting harder?"

Mark and Olivia contemplated the question and said that although some of the sacrifices had become easier, such as not having the subscription TV, and not going to coffee or golf, they were still struggling with each other, and Olivia really missed seeing her friends.

Derek did his best to encourage them. **"It is good to hear how you are coping with some of the changes. Olivia, you don't need to stop seeing your friends. Why not invite them over to your house rather than meeting at a place where you would spend money?**

Olivia had a million excuses in her head as to why she shouldn't invite her friends over.

Derick continued, "To cope with the frustrations, why not try out free activities in your area such as walks, picnics and outdoor gyms."

Mark could not think of anything that he enjoyed doing besides golf, but they both realised that Derek had shared some good advice.

Derick then asked, "Besides the struggles that you had during the month, how did you find your homework?"

Olivia was pleased to report that they had only spent three hundred and twenty-eight pounds and twenty-two pence on their groceries, and this was less than the three hundred- and sixty-pounds monthly limit Derek had given them. Mark reported that he had managed to sort out his three-hundred-and-sixty-pound debt with Philip through a loan from his mum, which meant that they only needed to settle it once they were in a better financial position, and he had not paid for any golf.

Olivia interjected, "…but you did play golf."

Derek frowned at Mark who was quick to respond, "Yes, but it was a work function, so I didn't pay for it."

After he'd seen Derek's relieved smile, Mark continued, "I have also started attending two support groups: Gamblers Anonymous and Alcoholics Anonymous. They are helping me to stay on track."

"Well done both of you," Derek said, pleased with their feedback. "And I have some more good news for you. The micro lender has agreed to reduce the loan by fifty percent…"

Mark interrupted with a groan. "But they should cancel it altogether!"

Olivia retorted: "Well it's better than I expected."

Derek patiently waited for them to finish speaking and then he continued: "Remember, although it is not the whole loan, a sizeable chunk has been written off."

Mark still wasn't satisfied. "Shouldn't we log a formal 'reckless lending' case against them to get the whole loan written off?"

"We could log a claim and we might win it," Derek said slowly, "but there is also the risk that we'll lose because of the false information you gave them when you completed the loan application form. However, it's your choice whether you accept the reduced loan or pursue the case."

Olivia placed her hand on Mark's arm. "Mark, the fifty percent will make a significant difference to our debt. We should accept the settlement."

He nodded and smiled. "You're right, we should take up the offer while it's on the table."

Derek continued, **"Mark, the micro loan company has also asked whether you wanted to reduce the monthly instalments now that the loan is smaller. My advice is that you stick to the original instalment amount because by doing this you'll pay the loan off even faster."**

"Sounds good to me," Mark said, and Olivia agreed.

"Right, I've worked out that the loan will be repaid within six months. I also looked at the possibility of consolidating some of your debt; however, with the reduced interest rates and the changes you are making to your spending patterns, this is not necessary."

Derek then said he wanted to introduce two new parts to their budget. Firstly, Mark and Olivia were to track their debts by writing down the balance owing on each of them and then recording every transaction associated with that debt, such as the repayment, interest, and admin fees monthly.

This way they could see exactly how much money they owed up to the minute and, more importantly, they could identify the smallest debt out of all the debts they had. This was essential information, because at the end of the month he wanted them to transfer fifty percent of their surplus, which was generated by sticking to their limits, into that smallest debt.

The reason for doing this, Derek said, was to pay that debt off as quickly as possible. Once they had paid off their lowest debt, their surplus at the end of the month would grow—this was an easy conclusion to make because once they'd paid their lowest debt, they no longer had to make repayments on it, thus freeing up more money.

"It's important to note," Derek highlighted, "that this is where the beauty of the strategy comes into its own. You'll then take the larger surplus and transfer it into the next lowest loan and will keep doing this until eventually you've paid back every loan. Mind you," Derek warned them, "although it seems simple, the hardest part will be to stick to the plan! Many people are tempted to use the monthly surplus on a new purchase, instead of using it to pay off existing debt."

"What about the other fifty percent?" Olivia asked, hoping that this was for them to spend as they wished.

"That money is for the second thing I want you both to do, and that is to create an emergency fund."

Mark interrupted Derek, "What for?"

"Well," Derek explained, "you need to set aside money every month and put it into a savings account for unforeseen circumstances. A safe amount to have in savings would be the equivalent to three months of your salaries, as this should be enough to help you if there ever was an emergency."

Olivia laughed. "The last time we had a savings account like that was before we bought our house. It didn't last long!"

Derek explained that this account would *only* be for emergencies. This way they'd avoid going into debt if something went wrong. "You must be disciplined and not use this fund to pay off any of your debts or for unnecessary expenses. Now, I know it sounds strange, but it is vital that you do this."

Olivia nodded her head. "It's a great idea," she said enthusiastically. "But it is such a small amount, how will we ever get to three times our salary?"

Derek reassured Olivia that time would take care of that; they need only to be disciplined and stick to the task at hand.

The plan sounded like pie in the sky speech, but both agreed to do it.

Derek closed the meeting by reminding them that their homework was to track their debts and to begin paying fifty percent of their surplus into their lowest debt at the end of each month, and the other fifty percent into a savings account for their emergency fund. The next meeting was scheduled for two months' time, and it would be over the phone.

21. The Breakthrough

Olivia and Mark were still struggling to adapt to their new lifestyle, but they found that reminding themselves that they were getting out of debt worked wonders on their resolve. Mark continued to go to the Gamblers Anonymous and Alcoholics Anonymous meetings to keep him on track. In addition, cutting back on takeaways meant that they were now eating far healthier meals.

However, they both felt edgy and were sorely tempted to veer away from the plan. Little Leonard was oblivious to what was going on and happily played with his baby toys on the living room carpet.

Eventually, Olivia said: "Mark, I'll go mad if we have to stay at home all the time!"

Mark groaned. "You're right Olivia, but where can we go? We have no money."

"Why don't we pack some food and go for a picnic?" Olivia suggested, getting up to look out of the window. "It's a beautiful day with clear skies, and we can go to the park."

Mark was not big on picnics, but it was the best idea that either of them could come up with. The time away from their troubles refreshed them both and Mark enjoyed the picnic even more than Olivia did. Leonard loved the ducks but was a little scared when they came too close. The picnic triggered a new closeness in Olivia and Mark's marriage, and from that day onwards they actively sought out amazing places that cost nothing to visit. One of their favourite outings was a nearby nature trail in the woods where Leonard could chase butterflies and (much to his mother's dismay) jump into every muddy puddle he could find. At the end of the month, they paid an extra one hundred and six pounds into their store card as this was the lowest debt. They had also managed to save one hundred and six pounds in their emergency fund. Olivia laughed as she realised that not only were they getting out of debt, but they were both far trimmer from all the exercise and healthy eating.

The next challenge was to speak to their friends. Over the past few months, she and Mark had said 'no' to so many invitations and she felt if she declined another one, she would lose a friendship. It was awkward but Olivia decided to be honest about her struggles with Amber, one of her closest friends. **As they chatted over coffee at her home, she was surprised to hear that Amber had financial struggles too. Loans were far too easy to come by and they created more problems than they were worth.** Surprisingly, Amber asked if she could join them on one of their picnics. Olivia agreed and at the same time realised that she had been silly to keep quiet about her financial woes, as she could have invited her friends to these picnics all along! 'Picnics with friends' proved to be immensely popular and soon became a regular event.

Olivia and Mark kept each other accountable as they worked through the latest homework. Initially any questions over what they had each spent money on had spilled over into fights, such as the time Olivia rang Mark to identify the eighteen-pound debit that had gone through his account. Mark was annoyed that she should question him and insisted that it was for business parking; he pointed out that his company would reimburse him when he put in a claim at the end of that month. Over time the fights eased, and they both acknowledged that being accountable to each other made it easier for them to stay on track.

These conversations about money were tough but they had to happen; without each other's support they would veer off the plan. They were both counting the pennies, and this made all the difference.

Two months after their last appointment, Mark received a reminder that his mobile contract was up for renewal. He knew that he had to downgrade to a smaller package as this would save another eighteen pounds a month, but he spent the rest of the day thinking about whether it was necessary. Mark felt that they were already saving money and getting out of debt, so what difference would eighteen pounds a month make?

That night the phone rang; Mark had been expecting it, as this was Derek's scheduled call.

"Hi Derek, how are you?" Mark asked enthusiastically.

Derek responded, "Everything is good! What about you?"

Mark was excited to give his feedback. "We're doing well. We have paid off some debt and our emergency funds are growing."

Derek was pleased to hear the news. "And how is Olivia?"

Mark replied, "She's in the next room—let me call her."

Olivia came to the phone and Mark put it on loudspeaker. "Hi Derek, so good to hear from you," she said.

Derek wanted to hear the latest on their journey and Olivia explained how far they had come. The excitement in her voice was palpable and she bubbled over about how fit they were because of their lifestyle changes. Their social life had also improved as many of their friends were now joining them for their picnics and nature walks.

"I must commend you for sticking to the plan," Derek said warmly. "Could you email your spreadsheet to me?"

Mark did that while they were still on the call.

As soon as Derek glanced through the spreadsheet, he said: "This is impressive! Well done to both of you, you are going to get out of debt in no time. Have you managed to downgrade the phone package yet?"

Mark was annoyed that Derek asked this and gave out an audible sigh.

"Mark, are you ok?" Derek queried.

Mark replied, "I was thinking of keeping the contract as we are already doing so well with the plan and can easily afford the additional eighteen pounds."

Derek replied, "Yes, I know that you are doing well and can afford to keep the contract, but you must consider that if you are going to compromise on one commitment, it won't be long before you start compromising on others as well."

It was a tough discussion, and Olivia was ready to pounce on Mark all through the conversation. When he eventually agreed to downgrade his package as it was the right thing to do, she was pleased that she'd held back and allowed him to make a great decision on his own. At the end of the call Derek encouraged them to persevere because before they knew it, they would be out of debt. He also advised them to continue with the plan and send him the spreadsheet monthly. Their next visit would be at his office in six months' time. The following day, Mark followed through on his commitment and got the smaller mobile package.

Three months later, Olivia and Mark were overjoyed as they had paid off their first micro loan! Mark arranged a dinner to celebrate their achievement.

Later in the afternoon, when Olivia arrived home from work after picking up Leonard from her mum's house, she was surprised to see a trail of rose petals on the floor beckoning her towards the kitchen; in the background she could hear a romantic song playing. Reaching the kitchen, she saw two large gifts on the table. One of them was addressed to Leonard who was trying to eat the rose petals, and the other had her own name on it. There was a letter attached and Olivia was surprised to see that it was a handwritten invitation to dinner.

I'll be there in an hour to pick you up.
Love Mark.

Just then the doorbell rang. Olivia was startled to see Deborah, the babysitter who had previously looked after Leonard during their appointments with the financial consultant, standing on the doorstep. Olivia let her in, and Deborah explained that Mark had asked her to look after Leonard for the evening as he was taking Olivia on a date. After saying hello to Leonard, Deborah encouraged Olivia to go upstairs and get ready.

Olivia raced upstairs, but turned around when she heard Deborah calling her. The babysitter was standing at the bottom of the stairs looking up at her.

"What's wrong, Deborah?" Olivia asked uncertainly.

In answer, Deborah handed her the beautifully wrapped parcel. "Don't forget your present!" she said with a smile.

Clearly Mark had said something to Deborah! As soon as Olivia opened the gift from Mark, she understood why Deborah had run after her. Inside the neat white box there was a beautiful dress—it was the same one she had had seen in the shop window a few weeks earlier while out walking with Mark. Olivia muttered to herself, "How on earth could he afford this?" but got ready anyway. The dress fitted perfectly, and she looked incredible. Olivia heard Mark's key in the lock and ran downstairs as he stepped into the hall. She melted into his arms, and he hugged her tightly.

"You two should go," said Deborah from behind them. "Leonard and I will be fine."

When she saw the limousine parked outside their house, Olivia wanted to ask Mark how much it had all cost, but she was too excited to spoil the surreal moment. The limousine was everything she had ever imagined it might be. The champagne flowed, and both Olivia and Mark felt like royalty. Twenty minutes later, the driver pulled up next to an exclusive seafood restaurant. She recognised it instantly as the one Mark had taken her to on their very first date.

That evening they laughed and cried more than they had done for many years. Mark spent some of the night apologising for who he had become before he had sorted out his life.

"I lost sight of myself, and I've been an awful husband to you and a terrible father to Leonard. Things are changing now, and I want you to know how wonderful you are. Thank you for standing by me—I don't deserve it."

Olivia wept as she listened to her husband. In just a few months, their marriage had completely turned around.

The evening was a welcome relief from all the stress. On the way home they promised to have a date night every second Thursday; they'd needed this time alone together and had really enjoyed each other's company.

That night was a turning point for them in working out the balance between doing the right thing with their money and having fun in the process.

Olivia felt that their marriage had reached an amazing place and there was now so much hope for their future. They had paid off the clothing account, the food account, and one of the micro loans. Mark's credit card was the next one on the list; however, when Olivia got a bonus in December that year, paying it into the debt was a tough decision. In the past, they had always used her bonus to go away on holiday and this would be the first year they'd broken the tradition. Olivia was sorely tempted to plan a getaway, yet she realised that this minor sacrifice would result in far better holidays in the future. Before she knew it, she'd transferred her full bonus into Mark's credit card.

He called her straight away. "Olivia, there's been a payment into my credit card—do you know anything about it?"

"Yes, that was my bonus," she said sweetly.

"That's incredible! Do you know that we are now in credit on the card by two hundred and fifty-three pounds?"

Olivia laughed out loud because another loan had been paid off.

Mark transferred the surplus into the emergency fund. They had now saved up three months' worth of their salaries, just as Derek had recommended. They worked out that if they could keep this up, they would be free from their short-term loans in no time at all.

A month after paying off the credit card, Olivia took a pregnancy test, and it was positive. They had discussed having a second child before, but now that she was pregnant, she wondered what Mark would say. That evening she waited anxiously for him to get back from work. As soon as he walked inside the hall, she raced into his arms and hugged him tightly.

"What's up Ollie?"

Olivia's voice was muffled as her face was against his chest. "Nothing—I just love you so much."

Mark knew there was more to this.

Olivia wanted the news to be a surprise and had put the pregnancy test on their bed so that Mark would see it as soon as he went upstairs. He always changed out of his work clothes when he arrived home, but that evening he stayed right where he was.

"Mark—aren't you going to get changed?" Olivia said, pulling away from him a little.

"Not just yet. First, I want to find out what is going on. Something about you seems different."

She quickly said she was just excited about how much debt they had paid off. Fortunately, Mark did not press the matter and soon went upstairs. As he sat down on the bed to take off his shoes, his fingers touched something unfamiliar. Lifting the piece of plastic, he gazed at the two stripes for a few seconds until he realised what it was.

Then he yelled out joyously: "We are going to have a baby!"

That same evening Mark handed Olivia a letter. He had been holding onto it until the perfect moment arrived, and this was it.

"This is for you Ollie."

Olivia took the envelope from Mark and reached inside. She pulled out a statement with 'PAID' written across it.

"That's the last micro loan paid off; we have no more short-term debt!" Mark said happily. "But there is still something else inside the envelope. It's for you, babes."

The envelope felt empty, so she tore it open to get a better look and when she did, she saw a small, folded statement taped to one of its sides—clearly Mark had intended her to read this last of all. Olivia gently removed the sticky tape to ensure that the paper did not tear whilst Mark fidgeted impatiently beside her. As soon as she'd read it, she burst into tears and hugged Mark tightly. Somehow, he'd paid off her vehicle as well, something that she'd never thought possible.

Through the tears she asked, "Where did you get all this money?"

"Do you remember the evening I took you out in the limousine?"

Olivia nodded.

"I am sure you wondered where I got the money for that."

She nodded again.

"Well, with all the lifestyle changes we had made, I started to work so much better than I had in the past. First, I got a small bonus from my boss for an important deal that I landed for the company, which I used for our celebratory dinner. Now, a week ago, I got the largest bonus I have ever received!"

The news was so refreshing that Olivia burst into tears. She knew they would be okay when their baby arrived.

22. The Future

Six months had passed since they'd last visited Derek and they were astounded at the improvements to the building. The lift was now working smoothly, and they soon greeted Cindy at her desk. The receptionist had Olivia's water and Mark's coffee ready.

Derek was waiting in his office, a huge grin on his face. He knew how well they were doing because Olivia had been sending through the spreadsheet every month, but he scarcely recognised Mark and Olivia; they were like completely different people.

He said, "What has happened to the two of you? Who are these people in my office?"

Olivia giggled. "We've got back to who we were when we first met! Somehow everything has clicked into gear, like a blockage being removed from a pipe."

Mark interrupted her. "I was that blockage!" he laughed as he said this. "I lost my way and now I'm back to being myself. It's obvious to me that our debt caused us to fight and blame each other for poor decision making, and now that we are making the right choices, we can focus on our relationship," he smiled lovingly at Olivia, "and enjoy life the way we did when we first fell in love."

Olivia added, "And we are having another baby."

Derek quickly said, "Congratulations! This is great news."

He then suggested that they chat about their long-term plans, as this was the last step of their financial recovery plan. They both agreed.

"Where and how would you like to live when you both retire?"

"We want to retire by the coast, and live close to nature and a golf course," Olivia said. It turned out that she had also begun to play the game, although she hadn't played in a while because of the pregnancy.

Derek took down quite a lot of information from them and then calculated what they would need to meet their retirement dream. **Most of the funds would come from their pension plans and he advised them that, based on the projections, they still needed a couple of hundred thousand pounds to reach their long-term dream.**

If they wanted to achieve their goals, they would have to increase their pension contributions and long-term investments.

Olivia and Mark both agreed to increase their pension contributions as this would have a positive impact on their taxable income and the tax benefit would also improve their ability to achieve their long-term plans. They also told Derek that they were thinking about buying a second property as an investment: they could rent it out to generate additional income. He liked the idea but cautioned them to consider the volatility of the rental market. It was doing well now but if for some reason they didn't have a tenant for a few months, they'd have to cover all the expenses for the second property themselves.

Lastly, Olivia expressed their wish to save for their children's education; not just for Leonard but also for the child that was still to be born. Derek showed them the available education policies and they chose the most suitable one.

Shortly before they were due to leave, Derek remembered to ask them whether they had a will.

Both Olivia and Mark replied, "Yes." The way their words synchronised made them all laugh.

"That's good," Derek said. **"It is important to have an up-to-date will as this ensures that should anything happen to you; your estate is given to those you've already decided should have it. Most importantly, it ensures that your children will be looked after.** I have heard of cases where both parents died without a will, and the grandparents couldn't agree on who would be the carer, so the child was put into social care and left there until the state decided which relative the child should go to. That scenario would be very traumatic for the child."

When Derek said these words, both Olivia and Mark realised that they had not written down in their will who would take care of Leonard, nor the new baby. The thought made them shudder.

Olivia burst out, "We must appoint someone to look after our children straight away!"

Derek looked at his watch. "I have time available now to continue the session if you're both up for it. This is such an important matter."

They agreed and he spent the next hour with them on their will.

The meeting had its moments, especially when Mark and Olivia had to decide on who the children's guardian should be, but they finally agreed that Leonard and the baby would live with Olivia's parents and that Mark's parents would have the right to visit as often as they liked.

Derek covered so many distinct aspects while drafting their will and both were extremely appreciative that he had done this for them. Leaving Derek's office that day they had real peace of mind as they knew that in the unlikely event of anything happening to either of them while the children were minors, the state would not be left to decide what to do, as their will was extremely specific. They also agreed to meet with Derek on an annual basis to review their investments, update their will, and ensure that they were still delivering on their long-term strategy.

Olivia and Mark were forever grateful to Derek for making such a difference to their lives; without his intervention they would still be struggling with debt.

Their beautiful daughter Gia was born a few months later, making their happiness complete. In the years that followed, Leonard and Gia were given the best that life had to offer. Mark and Olivia continued to follow through on their financial commitments and were able to achieve their retirement dream. Life was good.

Epilogue

In the book you may have wanted a different outcome for a few of the characters, such as Jason. Surely his story could have ended differently, after all just because you grow up in a difficult home, does not mean you will end up in debt and fighting everyone. Maybe you felt that Jennifer could have overcome her drug addiction earlier, or that she could have rebuilt her practice and become wealthy again, or maybe her parents could have stepped up and restored the wealth that she had lost. What about Emmanuel and his dream to study further, why was this dream never achieved, he had so much money in the end and could have afforded to study, so why didn't he? And what about Olivia and Mark, with all the conflict in the beginning of their marriage, divorce may have been the only option, and maybe you would have made a different choice to the one they made.

I too had all these questions when writing this book and had numerous endings to all their stories, such as Jason declining the loan and saving for the car leading to a very different life. I also had Jennifer following her dreams and starting a practice in Africa. I had Emmanual marrying a colleague at work and he never did get to study. Olivia got a divorce and had initially struggled to make ends meet and be a single parent to Leonard. There were so many different permutations based on the individual choices they made, much like the lives we lead today.

Then there was the question of adding actual examples of a bank statement, showing Jasons salary slip, the markers, and the budget for Olivia. I even thought about showing the clauses that were never read, maybe even Emmanuel's business contracts or Jennifers sale of her practice. In the end I decided to exclude these examples, for the simple fact that it would be easy to disqualify yourself from the mistakes they made, as when you see them, you may say, "That's not me, my loan is only a small amount," or "I don't have a computer so I can't build a budget like the one in this book."

I believe that in the stories there are truths that apply to all of us, sometimes we are a Jason and make reckless decisions in the spur of the moment, not thinking of their consequences. Sometimes we are an Emmanuel and are bitter and blame others for the struggles we are going through, rather than taking ownership for our own lives. We may even at times use some of our pain as a driving force to better ourselves just like Emmanuel did. We may also be a Jennifer at times, where on the surface everything looks ok, but deep inside there are problems that are impacting our ability to see clearly. We can even be like Olivia where we face challenges on our own but no matter how hard we try we can't overcome them. We need to reach out and ask for help, stepping out and being brave is the first step in getting back our financial freedom.

The emotional impact of our lives has a profound impact on our ability to make great financial decisions, and great financial decisions have a profound impact on our emotional wellbeing. Some may ask which came first, our emotional wellbeing leading to great financial decisions, or great financial decisions leading to our emotional wellbeing. I am not too sure, but one thing I am sure of, and that is that if a person does not manage their finances well, it always has an impact on their life.

No matter the ending of the story there are ten principles that I believe always hold true no matter which ending you would have preferred, and these are:

Principle 1: There is always a second chance.

Whatever age and stage of life you are in, nothing in your life is final: there is always the opportunity of a second chance. There are numerous examples of people, young and old, turning their lives around and you can do it too. Your 'second chance' is a result of making wise choices that will affect your present and your future.

Principle 2: You must earn money.

You can do this by running your own company or by working for someone else. For now, it doesn't matter whether the job is well-paid or not; this is just a starting point, it is not an end point. Sitting in your room doing nothing will not bring you money and all that will happen is that someone else who is earning money will have to look after you.

Principle 3: You must have a budget.

This will give you an awareness of your daily expenses, and it will help you to stretch your money so that it lasts through the month. If you spend more in a month than you earn, you will go into debt. Your budget should include food, transport, housing, electricity, water, clothing, giving, and savings. If you understand what you spend money on and you plan meticulously, you can ensure that you do not overspend. It's also good to include the category of giving (to your church or a charity) in your budget as helping others is what makes us human.

Principle 4: Debt must serve a positive purpose.

So many people do not realise just how expensive debt is. Many take short-term loans to fund their spending habits. This causes pain in the future when their personal debt gets out of control. There are so many advertisements enticing you to 'buy now pay later,' 'interest free for four months,' 'instant loan' and the like. In this frenzy you can get caught up in the moment and make the mistake of purchasing something you do not need. It is important to think about the cost of taking this type of loan *before* you decide to take it.

Loans are awfully expensive: this is due to both the interest that is charged and the fees. Short-term loans include things like personal loans, overdrafts, store cards, credit cards and micro loans. All of these are called unsecured loans as the organisation that you borrow from does not use your assets as collateral in case you do not repay the loan. In many cases people take short-term loans because they spend more money than they have earned, or they want something instantly for which they have not saved. Neither of these examples are good reasons to take a loan!

In some cases, there is a positive purpose for the loan, such as requiring money in the short term to finance your business expansion. However, the decision to take on debt must not be taken lightly as it is expensive and can quickly spiral out of control. Many have fallen into its trap and have spent months—sometimes even years—trying to get free.

Principle 5: Debt must be repaid.

It's essential to understand that if you do not repay the loan on time, the companies you have borrowed from will do everything in their power to get their money back. They will call you incessantly; they will tell you that your credit record is affected; in some cases, they will use legal means to gain access to your assets so that they can sell them to repay your debt. I have seen many, many people lose everything due to being overindebted.

Principle 6: You can get out of massive debt.

If you have a lot of debt do not give up hope because you certainly can get out of it. A good starting point is to consult a financial expert, as this person will help you to see where you are going wrong and what areas you can change. The process uses many different strategies such as negotiating longer payment periods for loans, cutting up your cards, cancelling unnecessary contracts, getting interest rates reduced and, in some cases, the provider may even agree to reduce the debt you owe. A great strategy to get out of debt is to pay off the smallest debt first and then use the freed-up money to start paying the next debt. The road ahead will be tough to navigate but as you change the way you live, the path will get easier, and you'll eventually reach your goal.

Principle 7: Save for the things you want.

The key is to know what you want, to have the commitment to save for it, and not to use debt to get it. This requires patience and resilience because along the way you'll often be tempted to use the money you've saved. These temptations will come in many different forms: friends invite you out when you know you can't afford it, or advertisements tempt you to buy something appealing.

Sometimes the temptation even comes from within your own mind, where you begin to crave things. If you live by the principle of always saving up for what you want, you learn to defer gratification and you are more likely to avoid these snares. Saving takes time. It also gives you time to unpack whether you are making an emotional purchase. During the months you save, you may find that the things you thought you really wanted, have lost their appeal. Savings can be for anything: an emergency fund, a deposit for a vehicle, a deposit for a house, or your retirement. If you become a saver early in your life you will certainly reap the benefits when you are older.

Principle 8: Policies can minimise risk.

Many years back, friends of mine had home insurance for the contents of their house. After a while they decided to cancel it as they thought it was a waste of money. Unfortunately, they had not expected thieves to completely empty their home a brief time later, and without insurance they were in a terrible position. Everyone stepped up to help them with furniture and electric goods and it was a very sobering time for them; how they wished they'd never cancelled their policy!

Insurance policies such as vehicle or home insurance may seem like a waste of money, and hopefully you will never have something go wrong, but, if it does, these policies are a life saver. It is also good to take out policies that will pay out in the future, such as a retirement policy, as this could reduce your risk of needing financial support from others during your old age. In addition, there are life policies that will pay out on your death; this may seem counterintuitive, but a life policy would certainly help your loved ones who are left behind, especially those who rely on your financial support.

Principle 9: Prepare for your long-term plan when you are young.

This may sound strange but when you focus on your long-term plans at the start of your working life, you have a lot more time to prepare for them. It is surprising how many people do not cater for their future self. The outcome of this is that when they are older and unable to work, they become a financial burden on their family. It is vital that you are forward-looking when you are young, as the earlier you save for your future, the more likely you are to be financially free when you are older. Any good financial advisor you speak to will bring your future self into the conversation, because only thinking about retirement when you are close to retiring could be too late and many have learnt that lesson the hard way.

Principle 10: Write a will.

When a loved one dies, it is a very traumatic time and when there is no will, this trauma is multiplied. Family members who are supposed to mourn together end up fighting over who gets what. The state steps in to work out what happens with the estate (everything that is left behind) and the worst-case scenario is when parents die without appointing a guardian for their children. All this pain can be avoided if we regularly update our wills. Most importantly, a will ensures that your wishes will be carried out when you're no longer there.

Acknowledgements

I would like to thank God for continuously creating opportunities and always giving me a second chance.

Thank you to my beautiful wife Lisa, the bedrock and love of my life. Your support and encouragement throughout the writing of this book has kept me going.

Thank you to my daughter Shea for proof-reading my entire book and giving such valuable feedback.

Thank you also to my son Luke who gave invaluable insight into Emmanuel's journey.

Thank you to my daughter Shiloh and my son Levi, who were both understanding when I was absent writing this book.

Thank you to the team in Ghana for being such a willing and open audience all those years back. The positive feedback you gave me was certainly a big factor in me writing this book.

Thank you to Kweku Bedu-Addo: you are an inspirational CEO, and I am so grateful for the impact you have had on my life.

Thank you to Brenda Burgess for the hours of editing.

Thank you to Sean Kelly for all the prayers and encouragement.

Thank you to my mum and dad, for all your love and support. I love you both so much.

End Notes

Why the Butterfly Effect of Money?
Edward N. Lorenz. 'Predictability: Does the Flap of a Butterfly's Wings in Brazil Set Off a Tornado in Texas?' Last accessed April 24, 2023.
Https://static.gymportalen.dk/sites/lru.dk/files/lru/132_kap6_lorenz_artikel_the_butterfly_effect.pdf.

About the author

Steven Jacobs has been in the banking sector for over thirty years. He's worked for organisations such as HSBC, Standard Chartered Bank, ABSA (when it was a member of the Barclays Group), Standard Bank, and Nedbank. He has enjoyed the privilege of living and working in England, South Africa, and Ghana.

Steven has been a guest speaker at Allan Lloyds Group's conferences on Customer Experience. In his private capacity he has delivered numerous lectures on improving personal financial health. Through these lectures and one-to-one consultations, he has developed a passion to equip young people with the skills they need to successfully manage their finances. He is the author of '*The New Manager: How to become a leader in 52 simple steps*', which was voted as one of the top six business books in 2016 by Ian Mann (MD at Gateways Business Consultants).

Steven's qualifications include an MBA (Oxford Brookes University), a Postgraduate Diploma in Financial Planning (Stellenbosch University), and a Certificate in Mortgage Advice and Practice (The London Institute of Banking and Finance).

Steven presently lives in England with his beautiful wife Lisa and their four children, Luke, Shea, Shiloh, and Levi.

Printed in Great Britain
by Amazon